PRACTICAL RAILWAY ENGINEERING

PRACTICAL RAILWAY ENGINEERING

Clifford F Bonnett

C. Eng., F. I. C. E., F. I. Struct. E.

Imperial College Press

ICP

Published by

Imperial College Press
516 Sherfield Building
Imperial College
London SW7 2AZ

Distributed by

World Scientific Publishing Co. Pte. Ltd.

P O Box 128, Farrer Road, Singapore 912805

USA office: Suite 1B, 1060 Main Street, River Edge, NJ 07661

UK office: 57 Shelton Street, Covent Garden, London WC2H 9HE

British Library Cataloguing-in-Publication Data
A catalogue record for this book is available from the British Library.

PRACTICAL RAILWAY ENGINEERING

ISBN 1-86094-012-9

Printed in Singapore.

This book is dedicated to my wife

JEAN

without whose support and encouragement
this book could not have been written.

Foreword

As we approach a new millenium, transport of people and materials takes on an even greater significance world-wide than it has in the immediate past. The birth and evolution of railways during the last two centuries has had an immeasurable influence on industrial, social and economic development.

Engineers of all backgrounds and professional disciplines have played a leading role in the development, operation and management of railways. In future the contribution of railway engineers should be even more significant.

I am delighted to be able to write this foreword to Cliff Bonnett's book. I have known him now for seventeen years. His wide experience 'on the ground' with British Rail, London Underground and Docklands Light Railway, over almost thirty five years, ensures that this textbook has a sure foundation.

Recent years lecturing on a part-time basis at Imperial College have also shown that Cliff is well able to communicate in a simple and concise manner. I commend this book to all who wish to get a good overview of Railway Engineering.

Tony M Ridley, CBE, PhD, FEng, FICE, FCIT,
Professor of Transport Engineering
Centre for Transport Studies
Imperial College of
Science Technology & Medicine
University of London

Preface

The need for this textbook arose out of the author's experience whilst co-ordinating the optional subject 'Railway Engineering Concepts' for the Intercollegiate MSc Course in Transport run jointly by Imperial College and University College, London University.

The stated objective of this optional subject is;

> 'To develop an understanding of the engineering concepts involved, for all disciplines, in the planning, design, construction, equipping, maintenance and renewal of all types of railway.'

The author quickly discovered that there are many textbooks which give detailed information on various aspects of railway engineering, usually confined to one or two main disciplines, but none that give a general 'broad brush' approach to the subject as a whole.

This textbook is designed to fill this gap, not only for the student on this or similar courses but to be a useful reference book to all who need to expand their knowledge in this field to cover a wide spectrum.

The author wishes to acknowledge extensive help he has received from many practicing engineers and in particular those who regularly have contributed lectures on this subject to students on the London University course.

Acknowledgements

The author wishes to express his thanks to the Professors, lecturers and staff of the Centre for Transport Studies of the University of London for the practical help given in the production of this textbook.

In particular, he would also wish to record thanks to the following external lecturers who have assisted with material outside his own railway practical experience:

Eddie Goddard
Chris Hardie
Dr. Bob Holmes
Chris Holmes
Dr. John Medhurst
Terry Mahoney
John Vint

Appreciation is also expressed to British Rail, London Underground Ltd, Docklands Light Railway Ltd, The Science Museum, the Institution of Railway Signal Engineers and the Permanent Way Institution for assistance with the gathering of facts, information and illustrations.

I am particularly grateful to Professor Tony Ridley who has been a great encourager and has written the Foreword during his very busy year as President of the Institution of Civil Engineers.

Contents

List of Illustrations

CHAPTER 1
Introduction

1.1 Early beginnings

In medieval times people mostly travelled by foot or horseback and any form of transportation was mainly for moving goods.

The first railways were laid down in the seventeenth and eighteenth century for horse drawn trains of wagons in collieries and quarries. These 'hauling ways' initially had a surface of stone slabs or timber baulks which soon proved unsatisfactory as the loads carried inevitably grew heavier.

As the Industrial Revolution progressed, the idea was developed further by adding cast iron or wrought iron plates to reduce wear on the wooden baulks. This evolved further to iron edge rails enabling the use of flanged wheels for the first time.

By the time steam locomotives came on the scene, in the early nineteenth century, wrought iron rails and later steel rails were developed which were strong enough to support these heavy axle loads without assistance from longitudinal timbers.

In essence the track itself, together with its supports, had and still has the basic function of safely transmitting the loads and forces imposed by passing trains to the ground beneath.

Various other civil engineering skills were also involved in the construction of early railways.

These included the building of bridges, tunnels and gravity walls as well as extensive earthworks and drainage.

Fig. 1.1. Early railway construction.

From these earliest days, there was a need to balance the requirements and interests of the various engineering disciplines involved. As an example, rolling stock design has a considerable impact on the design and maintenance of the fixed infrastructure and there needs to be mutual appreciation and close co-operation between engineers if the best is to be achieved in all areas. This may sometimes require compromise in certain disciplines for the good of the whole.

1.2 Development and diversification

On the early railways the Boards would invariably appoint an Engineer who would be responsible for all the engineering of the railway parts, both moving and fixed. He would often also be involved in the actual day-to-day operating of the railway. This had considerable advantage from a point of view of co-ordination.

As development of railways progressed, inevitably individual engineers became more specialised and there tended to be a loss of the overall or generalist view.

It is the specific objective of the author of this textbook to encourage a wider view in railway engineering matters so that better appreciation of each other's engineering requirements and constraints is achieved.

1.3 The customer

In any consideration of the various engineering functions of a railway, the needs and aspirations of the customer must always be kept in the forefront of the mind. The passenger's basic needs are to travel comfortably and to arrive safely at the destination reasonably on time. The freight customer needs confidence that his goods will be delivered safely and on time. Both want this service at a reasonable cost. All engineers and Operators need to work together to achieve this objective.

This seems so obvious and basic that it hardly needs stating. However 'departmental' and local interests can and often do arise which can jeopardize this simple objective and engineers and managers at all levels need to be on their guard.

1.4 The operator

If the customer's needs must be kept paramount then it follows that the Operator's needs in satisfying the customer's needs are also very important. Here however, there is room for manoeuvre. In satisfying the customer's basic needs, there is often more than one operational solution. In this case, it is incumbent on both the operators and the engineers involved to jointly consider all the valid options which are available. A good example of this is the consideration of carrying out week-end essential works either over a number of shorter possessions of the railway or over one longer week-end.

The operator must also be able to deal with emergencies during periods of engineering work and contingency plans must be drawn up for this.

Fig. 1.2. Underground railway construction at Blackfriars: 1871.

1.5 Overall planning

In constructing and maintaining any railway system infrastructure, there always are many activities which are carried out in each of the engineering disciplines which overlap onto other disciplines/activities. This is inevitable. Proper co-ordination and co-operation is necessary here. There are also, from time to time, items of work where there is considerable overlap or 'knock-on' effect. An example of this might be the requirement to renew a number of bridges on a certain line all of which carry signal cables or equipment which is nearing the end of life expectancy. Depending on relative costs in each area, an optimum programme could be drawn up jointly which would keep overall costs and disruption to a minimum in the long term. Similarly booking of long possessions to do work in one area might provide opportunities for other engineers to carry out other works at the same time, thus reducing expenditure overall. This type of co-operation is not always easy and does require a flexible attitude and acceptance sometimes of irksome restraints. However, maximum benefit of the whole must be the criterion.

1.6 Choice of route and level

In the earliest stages of planning of any railway, choices have to be made relating to the best route, and which parts will need to be elevated or in tunnel. The route will be largely dictated by traffic demands and existing physical constraints, although in some instances alternatives might be available where engineering and cost variations should be compared.

In such cases, ground conditions and water levels as well as existing building foundations and services must all be taken into consideration.

Again the level of the railway will be determined by existing physical constraints. It is essential, however, that all engineering implications are fully investigated and costed before any decision is made to construct a railway, either underground or on elevated structure.

For underground construction, full allowance must be made for the 'full life' costs of escalators, ventilation/air conditioning, lighting and other services, additional tunnelled accommodation for staff, fire protection and emergency exits etc. Disruption during the construction period of works in inner city areas is a factor that needs also to be taken into account when deciding whether or not to go underground.

Before adopting any form of elevated railway, a careful consideration on environmental issues including visual impact and noise as well as dealing with emergencies at high level is needed. Although elevated railways occupy less ground level space than surface railways, the stations often cover more relative area because of the need for stairs, ramps and escalators etc.

From an engineering point of view, alignments should also be as smooth as possible without steep gradients or tight curves to reduce wear on both the rolling stock and the track and to keep power consumption to a minimum.

1.7 Resources required

For the satisfactory operation and maintenance of a railway, certain basic resources are required, which can be grouped into human resources, fixed assets and mobile machinery. Inadequacy in any of these three sides of this fixed triangle will mean that good operation cannot be maintained, irrespective of the performance on the other sides.

Careful selection and adequate training of personnel at all levels is essential. On-going good relations with staff, both at National and local level must have a high priority. This requires constant attention at all levels of engineering management. As in any large organisation, individuals need to feel that they are valued and that they have a positive part to play in the running of the whole enterprise.

Fig. 1.3. Concourse and roof at Paddington.

The following chapters of this textbook deal with the outline requirements of fixed assets and mobile machinery that are necessary to satisfactorily operate and maintain a railway system. This relates to the various disciplines involved but it is vital to keep in mind that in all areas, adequate human resources are often the key to success or failure.

The intention of this textbook is only to give a general engineering overview of all that is involved in designing, running and maintaining a railway. Because of this, readers may require in certain areas to look deeper.

In an endeavour to point readers in the right direction, where this is the case, some details of extra reading have been provided at the end of some of the chapters.

CHAPTER 2
Station Layout

2.1 The customer and the design process

Stations on railway systems vary enormously in regard to their complexity, suitability and effectiveness but all, in one way or another, will have a direct bearing on the general well being of the final customer, the passenger.

Even a simple country halt with a single island platform can effect the comfort of the passenger if, for instance, trains are infrequent and there is no adequate shelter in bad weather, lighting is poor or the surface is inadequately maintained. On more complex stations where passengers change trains or interchange to other lines or modes of transport, poor design or maintenance of the interchange facilities can also have an adverse effect.

Similarly, such shortcomings can make operation of the railway, particularly during emergencies, very difficult and sometimes unsafe.

The investigations that followed the Kings Cross fire, revealed that there often can be inadequacies in the layout of the infrastructure which, coupled with lack of procedures and systems, may well prevent safe management of major incidents. In the UK the Railway Inspectorate, the Health and Safety Executive and the Fire Brigades play a significant role in producing and enforcing safety requirements which impact on the design of stations. No new railway infrastructure should be commissioned until all hazards and safety issues have been properly addressed.

Ideally, the customer's requirements should be set down in a brief prepared by the railway operator. These requirements will need to be interpreted into operational guide-lines which should form the basis of detailed designs. In practice, because the designer is likely to be closer to technological progress and changes in the regulatory framework, the final design will emerge only after the operator has been given the feasible options and opportunities available. The operator, as the representative of the customer, will then assess the operational and business implications of each valid option before a final choice is made. It is a common feature of project development that the desire of the customer to ensure maximum value for money conflicts with the engineer's instinct to minimise building costs and to get to the construction stage as soon as possible.

2.2 The need for standards

On any railway system there is a need to establish uniform standards for the design of stations. This applies to any system but is particularly relevant where new lines or stations are being constructed on existing systems.

There is little point in providing new stations with much higher standards unless there is some chance of adopting these standards in the long term on existing stations.

Perhaps a good example of this is the choice of width of platform. In the UK certain absolute minimum platform widths are specified by regulatory authorities but there may be good reasons for making platforms wider at selected locations. Such reasons would include places where overcrowding is more likely, where lack of crowd control is potentially more serious or where certain trains terminate, reverse or diverge. Clearly giving more space for these considerations needs to be investigated at all locations together with the effect that introducing a new line, service or interchange may have on other stations. In such a case, money may well be best spent in a number of locations instead of all at one new project.

The preparation of station standards at an early stage is time well spent. A good starting point is to consult the Railway Construction and Operation Requirements issued in the UK by HMSO or any other local requirements in other countries. Additionally standards adopted by similar types of railways in the same country, city or conurbation should be taken into consideration.

A useful device to ensure that better standards are always kept in mind and adopted when opportunity arises is to specify 'absolute minimum' standards as well as 'desirable' standards.

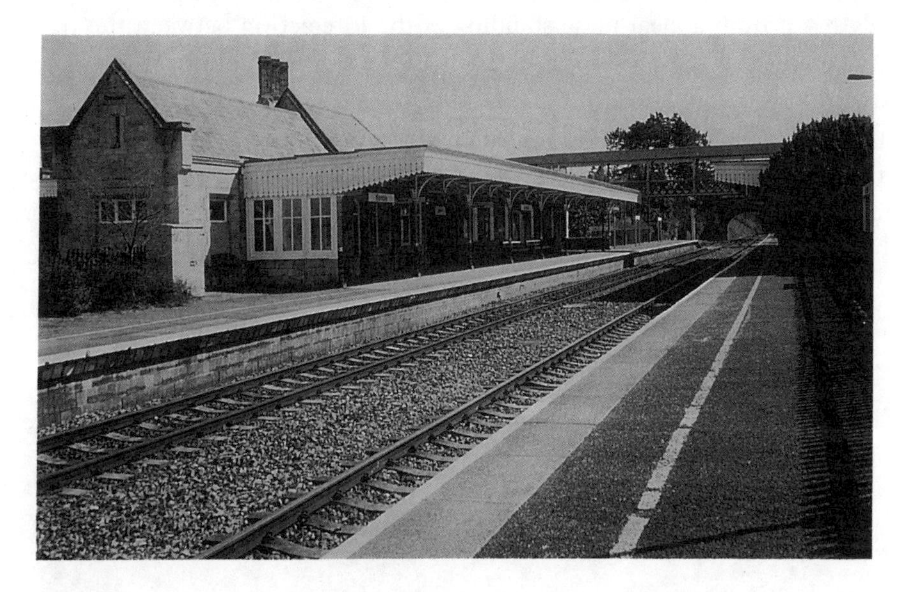

Fig. 2.1. Typical country station.

2.3 The objectives in station planning

In planning any station, the following objectives need to be kept very much in mind:

- Attractiveness in appearance
- Free movement of passengers
- Safe evacuation in emergency
- Access for the disabled
- Access for emergency services
- Safe accumulation and dispersal of crowds
- Reliable operation of train service
- Resilience to failure
- Cost-effective investment

Clearly these objectives cannot be achieved by provision of adequate space alone. A successful station is the product of well designed infrastructure, information and signing systems appropriate for the purpose, and a clear well promulgated management philosophy. A successful railway system will only result from a clear understanding of the interaction between the train service and the stations it serves, both in normal and abnormal operating conditions.

Station congestion may not always be remedied simply by the provision of more space. In many cases, the solution may often lie in running a different pattern of train service, different signing of passenger routes or the application of changed management methods.

2.4 The concept of speed and flow

The most important concept underlying capacity planning of stations is the relationship between the speed and flow of pedestrians.

Fig. 2.2. Typical sub-surface Booking Hall.

A great deal of investigation in this area has been carried out by J J Fruin and published in his book 'Pedestrian Planning and Design' (1971) to which reference should be made for more detailed information.

In his work, Fruin set down his observations of pedestrian walking speeds and flow rates for the full range from maximum, free flow, speed in unimpeded, uncongested conditions to totally congested conditions where movement is so impeded that speeds are reduced to a shuffle and flow to a trickle. It is interesting to note that peak flow takes place where walking speeds have reduced to about 50% of those achievable under unimpeded conditions.

For each of the elements of level walkway, staircase and queuing area, Fruin went on to categorise successive bands of density across the full range as 'Levels of Service' (LOS). LOS'A' represented low density and LOS'F' represented extremely high density. Typically LOS'C' or LOS'D' is considered appropriate for railway stations.

Other observations were taken both before and after Fruin, and all seem to roundly agree with his conclusions.

Fruin's terminology and data can therefore be accepted for the planning of most railway stations.

It is necessary therefore to estimate the likely throughput of passengers to various parts of stations and from that to decide sizes and areas on the information given herein and elsewhere.

2.5 The consideration of time

Time considerations underlie many aspects of efficient operation of a station and benefits to the passenger and operator alike will arise from the following:

- The layout of the station should promote the free-flow of passengers into and within the station complex. The provision of adequate space will maximise walking speeds and minimise congestion.
- Areas where passengers may stop or hesitate through uncertainty or need (e.g. to buy a ticket) need to be identified and space provided so that other passengers are not unduly hindered.

- In the event of service disruption, escalator failure or other unusual event, passengers must be able to accumulate safely until operational action can take effect.
- Future traffic growth can be accommodated.
- Emergencies can be controlled.
- Station signing is adequate.
- Infrastructure must be 'right first time'.

2.6 Planning for normal operation

The degree to which the business is prepared to invest in providing space purely for the added comfort of passengers must be decided by each railway system based on its own market position and objectives.

The starting point for any station planning is the demand forecast. This must be accompanied by a detailed knowledge of the likely train frequency from each platform and the time staff would need to take action when problems arise. Given working assumptions, it is then possible to determine how many people are likely to have accumulated within a particular area before control measures can be instituted.

The operator must determine his own relative values for key variables which combine to determine the minimum size and capacity for any element of a station.

These will include:

- time needed to become aware of a problem
- staff reaction and decision time
- action implementation time
- accumulation rate for passengers
- maximum density for safety

The frequency and destination pattern of the train service is also a key factor in the sizing of station infrastructure. Assuming, for instance, that the total staff reaction time is effectively five minutes and that the normal peak service is at five minute intervals, capacity at the platform must allow for at least twice the normal numbers expected in the peak.

2.7 The demand matrix

For complex railway stations, it is essential to understand where everybody is coming from and going to, not just within the station but in general terms outside the station. A typical example of such a matrix for Victoria Underground Station during an evening peak hour is as shown below:

To Zone From Zone	1	2	3	4	5	Total
1 British Rail	0	0	2280	948	470	3698
2 Bus/Taxi	0	0	1526	1301	0	2827
3 Victoria Line	7015	66	0	2748	806	10635
4 District	7219	751	4521	0	388	12879
5 Walk	0	0	2787	1780	0	4567
				TOTAL		34606

Fig. 2.3. Matrix of passenger flows, Victoria.

Where choice of route or exits and entrances exist it is important to determine the proportion of pedestrians likely to use each and allocate capacity in proportion accordingly.

The points in a station particularly vulnerable to a rapid increase in congestion are the platforms, foot of stairs and escalators and ticket halls.

If a service is scheduled to run at two minute intervals in the peak, a sensible guideline would be to assume that after five minutes delay of any train, some staff intervention would be triggered to control overcrowding. This translates into a design target of passenger density somewhere between one quarter and one sixth of that at which complete congestion occurs. In practice, it has been established that movement through restricted spaces ceases once the density gets to between four and five passengers per square metre. When passageways are almost empty average walking speed can be as high as 80 metres per minute but even medium 'bunching-up' to a density

Fig. 2.4. Congestion at the foot of an escalator.

of about two people per square metre dramatically more than halves the walking speed. In tabular form, the flow of pedestrians through walkways during differing degrees of crowding, can be as shown below:

Crowding (pedestrian/m^2)	Walking speed (m/min)	Max flow rate (pedestrian/m width/min)
0.5	75	38
1.0	65	65
1.5	50	88
2.0	35	92
2.5	28	80
3.0	20	60
3.5	12	40
4.0	4	16
4.5	0	0

Fig. 2.5. Pedestrian flows during crowding

It will be seen from the above table that overcrowding of any passageway beyond about two passengers per square metre of available space will have the effect of progressively reducing the throughput. The situation is worsened considerably if pedestrians are walking in two directions or have conflicting moves at junctions with other passageways.

It would be possible to design passageways on the basis of maximum crowding during peak periods of two passengers per square metre, theoretically giving maximum throughput for minimum widths. This however would be completely unacceptable as no incidents or train delays could occur without major crowding and disruption. At the other extreme, excessively wide passageways which are never filled to capacity cannot be justified.

What then is the sensible approach? Each railway system needs to select a design density for peak periods which will reasonably allow for minor incidents, delays and up to say three cancellations. It is essential in capacity planning of stations to offer sufficient resilience to train service perturbations and surges in demand that staff intervention by station control becomes the exception rather than the rule. This of course still calls for staff vigilance supported by modern surveillance and information techniques.

If a design figure for normal operational peak crowding of 1.25 pedestrians per square metre is adopted, sufficient resilience should be 'built-in'. As indicated by Fig. 2.5 this will mean that average walking speeds in the peak will be about 60 m per min. (2 mph) and for normal operation only about three quarters of the absolute flow capacity will be used. In the recommendations for size in the paragraphs that follow in this chapter the figure given above has been used in arriving at suggested dimensions.

2.8 Capacity requirements

It is recommended that the following limits should be applied to station areas for demand levels under normal peak conditions:

Platforms
Concourse areas } 0.8 sq m per person
Ticket halls

Passageways
one way – 50 pers/min/m width
two way – 40 pers/min/m width

Fixed Stairways
one way – 35 pers/min/m width
two way – 28 pers/min/m width

To allow for 'peaks within a peak' it is wise to use the calculated peak fifteen-minute flow figure which can be derived from the one-hour figure by multiplying by 0.3.

Similarly the peak five-minute flow figure can be derived by multiplying the fifteen-minute figure by 0.4. This five-minute figure should be used when testing the layout 'tight spots' to ensure that dangerous situations do not occur during the short lived period when crowding exceeds desirable levels at a restricted localised point.

The capacity of entrances and exits to street level should follow the guidelines above. From subsurface ticket halls/concourse areas there should be at least two exits to the street each of which must be able to take the full peak level demand albeit under crowded conditions.

Locations which are fed by exits from stations need to be examined to ensure that no bottle-necks exist immediately outside station buildings. This is particularly important where stations exit into Local Authority subways, shopping malls or where sporting events are likely to produce 'tidal wave' crowding.

2.9 Ticket halls

The location and size of station entrances will be determined by establishing the principal directions in which passengers may wish to leave or approach the station. In addition to determining passenger flows into and through the ticket hall, it is necessary to identify all activities which need to take place there. These will vary in scope and degree between main line railways, metros and light rail.

Additionally many large main line stations will have a mix of daily local commuters, long haul travellers and inter-modal transfer passengers. There will also be special cases such as at Waterloo where the requirements of Continental travellers need to be specifically met.

Similarly, any station which serves an international airport or exhibition centre will also have special passenger requirements, particularly with baggage handling/storage.

All ticket halls are likely to require space and facilities for the following as a minimum:

- Ticket selling and collection
- Meeting, greeting and waiting
- Travel information
- Retail and vending
- Station Management

Some may also require provision of:

- Toilets
- Public Telephones
- Baggage trolleys/handling and storage

In the sizing of a ticket hall, the following basic information needs to be established:

- the expected numbers involved in each activity
- their likely pattern of movement
- the duration of the activity
- the timing of activities relative to each other.
- identification of peak demands

From this information the basic size and layout of the ticket office and other facilities can be planned at the preliminary stage which must then be worked up to a final layout.

It is essential that space is provided for each activity in such a way that simultaneous activities do not hinder each other. For example, a poor feature of many existing stations is that queues of passengers buying tickets extend

Fig. 2.6. Different categories of passengers on a concourse.

across ticket barriers thus hindering access for ticket holders entering and leaving the station. This is not only a source of delay and irritation to passengers but can be potentially dangerous to passengers getting off crowded escalators on the approach to barriers.

Recent experience has shown that the critical dimensions for ticket offices are determined by the number of ticket gates required for the peak flow coupled with the number of ticket selling points required along the other axis.

If automatic ticket barriers are used then it is essential that an adequate number of gates is provided to cater for the expected passenger levels, both in and out. Automatic ticket checking gates should be specified to allow a throughput of at least 25 people per minute and it is considered prudent to allow for 10% of gates to be out of service. The calculation should be based on the five-minute flows plus 20 passengers.

In many locations there is a 'tidal flow' tendency, particularly at outer area suburban stations, between morning and evening peaks. In such places at least half of the gates should be reversible to allow for this.

The desirable overhead clearance in all ticket halls should not be less than 3 metres under suspended ceilings. Where this is structurally impossible at all points a reduction in clear height to an absolute minimum of 2.4 metres may be acceptable.

2.10 Access and interchange

By applying the various pedestrian planning parameters to the relevant demand figures it is then possible to determine sizes of passageways, staircases and escalators. These must be supplemented, however, by extra space provision which reecognises the inefficiencies in its usage in practice. These include the following:

'Edge Effects'

Passengers have a tendency not to make use of the full width available. People tend to keep a distance of at least 0.5 metres from the side wall. Thus passageway widths derived from flows need to have addition for edge effects, as do platforms.

'Hesitation and Decision Points'

It is also observed that passengers will often stop or hesitate when making a transition between one station element and the next while they decide what to do next. This hesitation may hinder other passengers behind them.

An additional 0.3 metres width should be provided in passageways where centre handrails are required to divide the flows. In no case should any passageway be narrower than 2.0 metres.

Where long distances have to be walked, consideration should be given to the provision of travelators. The preferred maximum gradient for a travelator for passengers is 1 in 20 but in very tight circumstances this may be increased to 1 in 12 as an absolute maximum. Run-offs of not less than 6 metres are necessary at either end of travelators.

An important feature is that passageways should be of constant capacity along their full length with good lines of sight avoiding as far as possible recesses and indentations which could form litter traps and possible hiding places.

It is very desirable that the ceiling height in passageways should be as high as practicable but generally not less than 3 metres. Where this is not achievable, a reduction to an absolute minimum of 2.4 metres may be permissible.

2.11 Stairs, escalators and lifts

In considering changes in level that have to be negotiated by passengers, the following guidelines should be adopted for new construction:

less than 0.5 m	Surface may be ramped (pref. max 1 in 20 abs. max 1 in 12.)
0.5 m to 3.0 m	Fixed staircase (min. 3 risers)
3.0 m to 5.0 m	Normally fixed staircase but escalator if cost can be justified.
Over 5.0 m	Normally escalator but outer suburban stations may have fixed stairs up to height of 6 m with two half landings.

Staircase dimensions must comply with the Building Regulations and the Department of Transport Railway Construction and Operation Requirements.

Escalators must comply with British Standard BS 5656 and particular attention must be given to provision of access to all equipment/machine rooms during traffic hours without obstructing passengers.

Passenger flow parameters for vertical circulation should be taken as follows:

- 100 people per minute for escalators one metre wide
- 35 people per minute for one-way stairs per metre width (clear)
- 28 people per minute for two-way stairs per metre width (clear)

The effective width of staircases is to be measured clear between handrails.

Stairs and escalators should generally be of open design with overhead clearances of at least three metres measured vertically from the pitch line of the steps to the soffit. In circular section shafts this dimension is to be measured from the point on the steps nearest to the shaft wall.

Any intermediate landing between flights of escalators must be sufficiently large to accumulate passengers safely while station staff effect appropriate action should an escalator break down.

2.12 Platforms

Station platforms are an important part of the infrastructure of any railway system and proper design can give great assistance to good operation. Critical to achievement of a tight timetable is adherence to the times assumed for boarding and alighting (dwell time). Failure to provide sufficient space on a platform may well mean the passengers waiting to board a train will not be able to stand aside for those getting off.

Fig. 2.7. Passenger movement during 'Dwell time'.

On a platform from which trains go to more than one destination, care must be taken to allow conditions in which passengers will not wish to take the first train to arrive. In these circumstances, even if the train destination pattern proportionately matches that of the passengers, the effect will be to drive up the average wait for each passenger and thereby increase the average crowding levels.

It is also important to vary the location of entrances and exits to platforms relative to the train, along the line of the route. This will have the effect of encouraging a more uniform distribution of passengers both on trains and station platforms, thus keeping dwell times to a minimum.

Platforms should be kept as straight as possible so that staff are able to see the full length in crowded conditions. Curves on platforms also have the effect of increasing the gap between the platform and the train which can bring attendant hazards. Ideally curves at platforms should not be less than 1000 metres radius. The stepping distance between the platform and the train should not exceed 150 mm laterally.

The width of platforms must be carefully considered for each system, taking into account the likely heaviest loading of trains, their frequency, the number passengers likely to be alighting and the number of exit points along the length of the platform.

The absolute minimum width of any platform should be limited to not less than two metres. This should only be accepted at minor stations and at platform ends or for very limited lengths away from passenger exits or entrances.

The desirable minimum width of platforms for fairly busy stations is three metres for side platforms and six metres for island platforms with tracks on both sides.

Headroom on platforms should be not less than three metres wherever possible.

2.13 Footbridges and subways

At surface and elevated stations, footbridges or subways will need to be provided to and from platforms. The limiting dimensions of these should be as those already indicated for passageways and stairs.

2.14 Station canopies

The extent to which platforms need to be covered needs to be carefully considered for each station. Clearly, it is desirable that some protection from the elements should be provided for waiting passengers but the cost of this provision can be high, including the on-going maintenance liability.

Estimation should be made of the maximum number of waiting passengers likely to be on a platform during peak periods. If it is not considered necessary for the canopy to go the full length of the platform, the lengths nearest to access points and station buildings should be covered.

At suburban stations where the main flow of passengers board and alight at different platforms, some economy may be effected by reducing the length of the canopy on the main arrival platform as passengers will generally disperse quickly and not wait.

2.15 Access for disabled passengers

In recent years, railway operators have started to consider specific provisions for disabled passengers, particularly those in wheelchairs.

In the past it was often thought impractical for wheelchairs to be used on railway systems, particularly where there are changes in level and crowded conditions. Many railway authorities banned them from their systems because of the perceived hazard they represented both to themselves and to other users.

In line with changing attitudes to disabled people, supported by European Directives aiming to promote mobility of all, railway authorities are increasingly reconsidering the position on this aspect. Several new Metros and Light Rail systems have been designed to specifically accommodate disabled people. Where new lines are added to existing systems there is considerable difficulty in ensuring that access is properly limited to areas of the system where it is safe for disabled passengers to go.

As well as concern, for passengers who are disabled there is now an increasing awareness that 'mobility impaired' passengers also have a strong need to be considered.

Fig. 2.8. Lift for the Disabled on Docklands Light Railway.

This group, which at some periods and locations is quite a significant proportion, includes the partially sighted, the elderly, mothers with small children and laden shoppers or tourists.

This change in attitude means that new station design must not preclude use by disabled passengers either at the present if it is safe for them to use the rest of the system or in the future when it is so.

Many small improvements can be made in detailed design which will assist those who have hearing and sight difficulties or who find walking long distances difficult.

2.16 The 'Downgraded' station

Even on the best operated of railways, there will be times, both planned and unplanned, when parts of a station become blocked or unusable. The planner and railway engineers need to think through in advance how a given station layout will function in such an event.

Downgrading of the general efficiency of a station as a whole could be triggered by many things. This would certainly include for instance:

- Escalator short term failure
- Escalator long term replacement
- Stair closure (e.g., tread or handrail failure)
- Automatic ticket barrier failure
- Train service disruption
- Partial blockage of vital connecting narrow passageway (e.g., caused by illness of passenger)

Where it is found that this partial downgrading of certain station facilities could cause major disruption, the planner should seek to improve the situation. Considerable skill is called for in this process to ensure that the best overall value for money is obtained. In the final analysis, there will always be a need to compromise between the solution which is the most economic for normal operating conditions and that which may not be ideal but does give more flexibility when things go wrong.

2.17 Planning for hazards

In the design of any railway station, consideration must always be given to major hazards that might occur within the station environment.

With all railways, but in particular for those which are beneath the surface, fire is the hazard which most influences station design. Fire presents a time-critical event in which passengers must be evacuated before the environment becomes incapable of sustaining life.

It is essential that all evacuation routes are well signed and are adequately protected where necessary by powerful ventilation systems, smoke/fire doors and roller shutters. It is also necessary to fully consider both the case of a train on fire and other stationary equipment such as escalators. In such an event, alternative escape routes must also be properly signed.

In dealing with a major life threatening emergency, such as a train on fire in a station, the target should be to be able to clear passengers from the immediate area of the train (the platform) in four minutes and from the station within six minutes. In a large or complex station, this last requirement would apply to another fire separated route or area rather than the station as a whole.

In the planning stage, it is essential to discuss with the local emergency services how their equipment and personnel will be given access to and from a major incident.

2.18 Staff accommodation

At the earliest stage, station designers will need to establish the accommodation , storage and office requirements of all the staff who will be involved in operating, engineering and maintaining the railway. This probably will include provision for those involved in the following functions as a minimum:

- Operation and Train Control
- Signal Engineering & Communications
- Permanent Way
- Premises and Structures maintenance
- Mechanical/Electrical/Escalator maintenance
- Cleaning

Some thought also needs to be given to accommodation which may be needed for emergency services in the event of a major incident.

2.19 Designing for maintenance

An essential part of the design of any station is the careful consideration of maintenance. A fully successful design is one that not only achieves the obvious requirement of allowing passengers to move freely between points but maximises the net worth of the business.

This is achieved both by attracting customers, thereby increasing revenues, and by minimising the lifetime costs.

A common failing of many stations on existing railway systems is that they now consume large resources in maintenance which can only be carried out at night or by closing the facilities to passengers.

In particular, each engineering department involved needs to be consulted relating to their proposed pattern of works which will be required to keep the railway fully operational. These works will generally fall into three general headings:

- Minor 'house-keeping' maintenance
  These will be normally carried out on a daily, nightly or weekly basis.
- Seasonal maintenance items
  Work that will be programmed like light bulb changing or track tamping on a yearly or six monthly basis.
- Long term renewal
  Replacement of life expired components like light fittings, stair treads or pit blocks.

Care needs to be exercised in the original design to ensure that, wherever possible, equipment is accessible without the need for possession or night work. Additionally, areas on platforms and elsewhere need to be able to be made available for storage of plant and materials for essential maintenance works.

CHAPTER 3

Rolling Stock

3.1 The definition of railway rolling stock

It is always useful at the outset of consideration of a subject to pause for a moment and to ponder the definitions, attributes range and scope of the matter.

Rolling stock used on railways in the earliest days evolved from carriages and wagons which ran on highways to carry both people and bulk materials. As early as the sixteenth century wooden wheeled carts were used in mines and quarries running on longitudinal timber rails.

With the progressive evolution of the skills and crafts of the wheelwright, metalworker and the ironmaker, wheels improved through various phases from simple rough turned wooden spools through spoked and rimmed construction to fully cast and turned metal wheels.

Similarly, body construction and springing, particularly for passenger carrying vehicles, relied very heavily on the experience gained in the construction of stagecoaches in the seventeenth and eighteenth centuries. At the end of the eighteenth century, horse drawn trams running on metal rails began to appear in a number of European cities. These horse drawn tramways were literally to pave the way for development of railways when steam power began to be developed early in the 1800's. One has only to look at illustrations of early passenger coaches to see how closely they resemble the road vehicles of the previous century. (see Fig. 3.1.)

Fig. 3.1. Early flanged wheels on iron rails.

As railway experience was gained, the design of rolling stock also evolved. Springing, body structure, wheels and axles all are subject to varying loads and stresses, when comparing slower speeds on rough roads to much faster speeds on railways, with a comparatively smoother ride.

Railway rolling stock generally runs on hard wheels on hard rails. The wheels are not only supported by the rails but are guided by them. The only exception to this is for a small number of metros where rubber tyres have been introduced. In this case the supporting function of the rail may be separated from the guiding function.

In all cases, railway rolling stock will transmit vertical, horizontal and longitudinal forces to the track and its supports. Most railways have adopted twin rails and flanged wheels. Forces are transmitted to the rail structure either by direct bearing on the rail top from the wheel tyre, or by bearing laterally through the flange, or by longitudinal friction. Potential 'overturning' forces caused by centrifugal force on curves, coupled with wind forces on

Fig. 3.2. The age of steam.

exposed locations are resisted by vertical dead weight and super-elevation or 'cant' on curves.

3.2 The range of railway rolling stock

Today there is a very wide range of rolling stock used throughout the world on different railways. This range includes the following basic types:

- Locomotives
- Freight wagons
- Passenger coaches
- Multiple units (with motive power in-built)
- Metro cars (usually multiple units)
- Light rail/Trams (usually articulated units)
- Railborne machines (cranes, tampers etc)
- Inspection and maintenance trolleys

3.3 The evolution of steam motive power

As has been mentioned previously, the harnessing of steam power in the late eighteenth and early nineteenth centuries was the springboard for the development of railways throughout the world. The concept of running hard rimmed flanged wheels on narrow metal rails had been tried out in the mines and quarries and found to be both workable and advantageous.

The main limitation to the effectiveness of using plate-ways, rail-ways or tram-ways was the adequate provision of haulage power or what became known as 'motive power'. Walking pace motive power was first provided by men and horses and later in some places by stationary engines driving winches for cable hauled cars. As the design of wheels, axles and bearings steadily improved, towards the end of the eighteenth century, heavier loads could be moved and rail borne movable steam 'locomotives' became a possibility.

The first steam hauled train was operated by Richard Trevithick's steam locomotive in South Wales in 1804. While this locomotive seems to have worked quite well on a mine tramway, the cast iron plates that formed the track proved to be inadequate for the heavier loads and impacts.

Hard on its heals, William Hedley's 'Puffing Billy' built in 1813, ran on a tramway near Newcastle-on-Tyne giving successful service for over forty years.

The first use of steam for a passenger train was George Stephenson's 'Locomotion' on the Stockton and Darlington Railway in 1825.

There is a wall plaque at the original railway station at Stockton which reads:

> 'Here in 1825 the Stockton and Darlington Railway Company booked the first passenger thus marking an epoch in the history of mankind'

The first public railway to use steam motive power exclusively and to run a regular passenger service was the Liverpool and Manchester Railway which commenced operations in 1829. This railway was perhaps the first to have the essential elements of a modern railway. All trains were locomotive hauled, running to a timetable, operated by company staff and only stopping at stations manned by its own staff. The railway linked the two cities and was only 38 miles long, taking about two hours six minutes to do the journey. This average speed of 18 mph seems extremely slow to us but when compared to walking, running, or going by narrowboat or stagecoach, was a substantial improvement.

What is even more amazing is that fourteen short years later Daniel Gooch, locomotive superintendent of the Great Western Railway, drove Prince Albert home from Bristol to London in about the same time, a distance of about 118 miles! The average city to city speed on that journey of 57 mph is still remarkable and could not be achieved today by driving from Bristol to London, even with the fastest car, without breaking the speed limits!

During the rest of the nineteenth century, railways continued to develop and spread to all parts of the civilised world. With this development, both steam locomotives and all types of rolling stock grew in size and complexity.

Steam power dominated traction on most of the worlds railways in the first hundred years or so. Indeed, until the 1880's steam was the only form of motive power that was considered viable for railways. Even the so called 'atmospheric' railways still relied on stationary steam engines to provide their power.

In the very earliest days, even at the time of George Stephenson's 'Rocket', boilers were fitted with multiple tubes, water space round a fire box and a fire which was drawn by the exhaust steam blasted up the chimney. Most locomotives had two cylinders linked to the large driving wheels by external connecting rods.

Cylinders were normally inclined at an angle to the horizontal and drove only one pair of wheels. Eventually cylinders were placed horizontally in a forward location and the driving power was linked to all the 'driving wheels' by various cranks and connecting rods.

There was also a great deal of activity in the design and evolution of valve gear, slides, pumps and pistons which all added to both the efficiency and the complexity of steam locomotives. Steam traction is simple in essence and some complexity led to more difficulties and problems than were solved.

The invention of 'super-heating' of steam in the late nineteenth century led to adoption of this feature in later steam locomotives giving rise to higher efficiency but also a need for better maintenance, particularly of boilers and tubes.

Early underground railways adopted steam power for hauling trains because at that time there did not appear to be any practical alternative. The first underground railway in the world was opened by the Metropolitan Railway Company in 1863 between Paddington and Farringdon, London. By that time many hundreds of miles of main line railway had been built around the world and over thirty years experience had been gained in the design, manufacture and operation of steam locomotives.

This original section of the new line, together with its later extensions (now the Circle Line), was constructed using the 'cut-and-cover' method. As the construction was only at a shallow depth, openings were left wherever possible in an attempt to ensure that steam, smoke and fumes were adequately ventilated.

The original intention was to use conventional steam locomotives on this line burning no fuel on the underground sections but relying on the 'head of steam' and heating up only at the end of the comparatively short underground section.

Fig. 3.3. Euston Square Station showing ventilation openings.

When the line was opened, it was found that conventional locomotives caused distress to passengers and staff due to the discharge of carbonic oxide gases. Some relief of the problem was found in construction of condensing engines but clearly some other form of motive power would be desirable underground. The London commuter had to suffer the inconvenience of steam locomotives in confined spaces for another three decades or so before a satisfactory alternative was found.

3.4 The advent of electric traction

The possibility of electric traction was first demonstrated by a Scotsman called Davidson in 1834 but it was not until the Berlin Exhibition of 1879, that the idea was developed far enough to show that it could be a practical challenger to steam.

Fig. 3.4. An early underground DC electric locomotive.

The obvious advantages of electric traction over steam for underground railways attracted the attention of many engineers and operators around the world in the last decade of the nineteenth century.

The first 'Tube' line to be built in London was the City and South London Railway between King William Street and Stockwell in 1890 using electric traction. This was followed within ten years by the construction of the Central London Railway from Shepherds Bush to Bank, also using electric traction. Other tube lines followed rapidly all of which were incorporated into today's London Underground.

Most of these early tube lines followed the main line practice of a single locomotive pulling non-powered carriages or cars. The City & South London locomotives were small four wheeled vehicles whereas the Central London Locomotives were much larger 'camel back' design with four driving axles mounted in two bogeys.

During the first decade of the twentieth century, all of the London tube lines departed from the principle of single locomotive hauling to using a

Fig. 3.5. A modern multiple unit tube train.

number of motorcars along the length of the train. This has considerable advantage for rapid transit trains, not the least of which is to distribute both traction and braking along the full length of the train. This has the effect of improving both acceleration and braking which is important on lines where there are frequent stops.

For the same reasons many main line railways have now come away from the use of locomotives for suburban and stopping services and have adopted multiple units with motors distributed along the length of the train.

3.5 Development of electric traction

The suburban and underground railways that were built or electrified in the early part of the twentieth century adopted a medium voltage direct current supply system which involved fairly costly fixed equipment but kept the locomotives relatively simple and cheap. A large number of transformer 'sub-stations' were involved with comparatively heavy conductor rails set

Fig. 3.6. Southern Region (BR) Multiple DC stock.

at track level. Technology was very similar to the early electric tramways which were also powered with direct current.

In the UK, London Underground and a large part of the Southern Region of British Railways adopted DC electric traction many years before the rest of BR converted from steam power to diesel power or seriously considered large scale electrification.

Overhead supply of high voltage alternating current was pioneered largely in Switzerland after the First World War and by the 1930's became the normal system of electrification on the Continent.

Fig. 3.7. Channel Tunnel stock which can run on either third rail DC or overhead AC.

High voltage AC electrification was not introduced to British Railways until after the Second World War. Since then, it has become the preferred system for surface railways. High speed AC electric locomotives have a high power/weight ratio as they carry no heavy fuel.

3.6 Diesel traction

This alternative form of motive power was invented by a certain Doctor Diesel of Berlin in about 1893. There are certain technical problems associated with applying diesel power to railways. These mainly relate to the fact that the engine must be turning even when the locomotive is stationary, unlike the steam engine which has latent power, provided the head of steam is up. In road vehicles, this can be overcome by the familiar mechanical device of introducing a clutch and gearbox. This works well for vehicles of moderate horsepower but is unsatisfactory for more powerful engines.

Because of this drawback, the diesel engine was relatively late in coming to the railway scene. It was not until the 1930's and later that the diesel began to be taken seriously and only in the 1950's that diesel and electric traction finally ousted steam in most parts of the developed world.

Two main methods of coupling the diesel engines to the driving wheels were evolved and still remain today.

Fig. 3.8. A modern Diesel-electric locomotive.

The first involved hydraulic drive which had modest success. Most of this type of locomotive originated from Germany and many are still running today.

Without doubt however, the standard diesel locomotive today throughout the world is the diesel-electric. One could describe this as an electric locomotive with its own on-board diesel generator power station.

The solution of the drive problem is complicated and therefore expensive. As a very rough indication of this, the first cost of a diesel locomotive is about three times the cost of a steam locomotive of similar power. However the real savings come to light when considering the 'whole-life' costs involved in running and maintaining steam verses diesel.

In particular, steam requires many man-hours each day before and after working to get up the fire and rake out the ashes etc. The diesel locomotive has immediate push button power and has a much lower requirement for 'down-time' for regular maintenance.

3.7 Evolution of wheel layout

The earliest steam locomotives had two or three axles, one or more of which carried the driving wheels. Richard Trevithick's locomotive had an ingenious arrangement which connected the two driving axles to the driving pistons by means of a series of large cog wheels.

In many cases, the inclined cylinders drove one pair of large driving wheels directly and these were sometimes linked to other wheels with 'connecting' rods. As locomotives grew in size, weight and power additional wheels were introduced largely to carry the extra weight of water and coal which was needed for the ever increasing journey length. Locomotive designers needed to get as much weight onto driving wheels as reasonably possible to avoid wheel slipping or spinning, a characteristic of steam engines. Heavy individual axle loads however were most undesirable from the point of view of supporting brides and structures. As in all engineering design, this has always meant that some compromise needs to be made between operational desirability and practical structural considerations.

The introduction of electric and diesel multiple units has allowed the use of many more driving wheels along the length of a train, thus reducing the adhesion, acceleration and braking problem.

3.8 Changes in locomotive maintenance practices

Steam traction involved the procurement of many extra locomotives because of the large amount of cleaning, lubrication, descaling and minor repairs that were necessary.

This resulted in all engines spending a considerable proportion of their life in the shops or sheds instead of out on the railway pulling trains. Additionally there was a lot of time spent in firing and other preparation before each day's working.

It was these considerations, amongst others, that led in the UK and many other countries to the demise of steam and the gradual introduction of diesel and electrical power, since the Second World War.

Diesel and electrical power has also enabled designers to dispense with large driving wheels and to introduce power driven bogies.

Also in recent years both locomotives and multiple units have been designed with motive power packages and self contained units that can be removed or replaced for maintenance. This has the effect of reducing yet further the amount of time that trains or locomotives have to be out of service.

3.9 From passenger 'Carriages' to the modern carbodies

Early sketches show that the Liverpool and Manchester Railway started operations in 1829 using stage-coach bodies mounted on four wheeled trucks. Third class passengers were often carried in simple wagons very little different from 'cattle trucks'. Sometimes as many as three or four stage-coach bodies were mounted on one truck with the seats 'facing or back' towards the engine. The doors on these early coaches were on each side, one per coach compartment, with no connection between the compartments.

The carriages on suburban stopping trains on BR retained an element of the same layout with individual unconnected compartments and single 'slam' side doors for well over a hundred years.

As railway journey times and distances increased, this quickly evolved for 'express' trains, with the introduction of a side corridor, to the basic carriage layout which remained normal for main line railways in the UK to the 1960's.

Fig. 3.9. Typical 'Slam door' compartment stock.

Early American railways, however, adopted the open coach with passengers sitting each side of an open corridor, boarding and alighting from the train through doors at the ends.

Many of the world's railways have now adopted the open plan for both main line and suburban services with doors at carriage ends and walk-through connection down the full length of the train.

Most metros and light rail systems have open plan layouts in the cars. In this case however boarding times are critical and doors only at car ends would be too restrictive. In this case there is a very fine balance between the number of doors and the number of seats provided.

The levels and curvature of platforms also has an effect on the design of cars and this varies considerably around the world. Increasing consideration is being given to the need to accommodate disabled passengers, especially those in wheelchairs.

Fig. 3.10. Modern open plan Main Line coach.

Fig. 3.11. Docklands Light Railway stock.

3.10 Carbody structures

Since the earliest days of railways, carbody structures have evolved and become considerably stronger, lighter and more economic. As mentioned previously, the earliest carriages were largely of wooden construction. These proved to have a very low crash resistance when accidents occurred with a high rate of injury and loss of life.

As early as 1840, in the UK, the Railway Inspectorate was set up to inspect newly constructed railways and to certify fitness for public travel. Various accidents investigated by the Inspectorate over the years have led to progressively higher standards being set for the design of rolling stock.

The first stage was to introduce a wrought iron and later steel underframe which fully supported the wooden superstructure. This system lasted well and was still being used in new stock up to the 1950's. The main drawback was that all the strength was in the chassis which performed well in collisions but body work splintered, still causing much loss of life and physical injury.

The next stage was the use of a steel underframe with steel or aluminium framing to the superstructure. This performed much better in crashes but the whole design was getting very heavy and expensive.

Modern cars and coaches are designed on the 'Monocoque' principle. In this case the whole structure is designed as a single monolithic unit, spanning between the main bogie supports. The structure then takes all the bending, shear and torsion stresses as an entity.

The final form is usually a composite of aluminium extrusions and welded stainless steel with a 'stressed skin'. All loads and stresses are distributed between the various components. The resulting design is considerably lighter than the previous design and is much akin to aircraft structural design. The lighter design coupled with higher stresses and repeated loading means that fatigue considerations become increasingly important.

Summarising, these developments of carbody design over the last almost two centuries are characterised by:

- Lower mass
- Higher stiffness
- Higher strength

These rolling stock characteristics lead to

- Lower energy consumption
- Greater crashworthiness
- Higher passenger comfort
- Higher passenger/carbody mass ratio

3.11 Main line train performance issues

When considering the engineering of a railway from the rolling stock point of view, train performance demands and issues need to be fully considered. These vary according to location and whether or not it is Main line, Metro or Light Rail.

The performance issues on Main Line railways for consideration are as follows:

- Is the traffic mainly one type (e.g., high speed express passenger) or mixed speed and type?
- What will be the impact on the long distance passenger carrying capacity of the railway of slow freight and stopping trains?
- What capacity will the signalling allow?
  (This will depend largely on such factors as the length of the signalling sections and whether there is uni-directional or bi-directional signalling.)
- Are there many passing loops or 'slow line' platforms at stations of secondary importance, to allow expresses to pass?
- What acceleration, braking characteristics and tractive effort is required to ensure that trains can work to desirable timetables?
- What are the maximum gradients on the line?
  (These will effect the previous consideration greatly.)
- How many speed restrictions are likely and what recovery will be required of time lost?

3.12 Train performance issues on metros and light rail

Generally metros and light rail systems only carry passengers and there is not therefore the added complication of 'mixed' traffic. Similarly, in most cases, there is no segregation of express and stopping trains to complicate matters. The main concern is to provide trains which will closely match demand at various times of the traffic day in the most economic manner. The main issues therefore are:

- What capacity is required at various times?
- What are the achievable acceleration and deceleration rates?
- What 'dwell time' is required at stations?
- What top speed is necessary?
- How can energy be conserved in normal running conditions e.g., by coasting?
- How much scope is required for recovering lost time in the peak due to delay?
- For light railways only, what additional factors need to be taken into consideration for any lengths of track which are incorporated into the highway and where 'shared running' takes place?

Once all these considerations have been fully investigated, decisions can be made on the type and number of different units of rolling stock that is required to run the railway. To this must be added extra stock to allow for the fact that there will always be some vehicles on programmed repair and maintenance as well as others out of service for unplanned reasons or mishaps. With modern rolling stock and proper maintenance procedures, this extra proportion should be able to be kept to not more than a quarter, depending on the size of the fleet.

It can often be shown that a small amount of extra capacity, both in tractive effort and braking, can play dividends in the long run and allow overall economies in energy.

For relatively short distances between stops, the timetable for trains running normally should allow for a pattern of motoring up to maximum allowable speed and then coasting for a period before braking for the next station. This pattern is less demanding on energy than flat-out speed and maximum braking which can however be resorted to if lost time needs to be regained due to delay.

3.13 Freight rolling stock

Early railways were characterised by 'goods' trains of a very mixed variety. In the days of steam, it was commonplace to see long trains of mixed wagons carrying coal, stone, timber, slate and many other basic materials needed both in the large cities and in the smaller towns. The operation of such trains was often slow and labour intensive, involving marshalling yards and painstaking 'shunting' and off-loading.

Economic considerations have caused such operations now to be a thing of the past. However, railways are still an excellent way of moving freight especially in large countries where distances are much greater. Even so approaching two hundred million tons of freight a year is still transported on the railways in the UK.

Fig. 3.12. Specialised freight wagons

Freight wagons in recent years have tended to become specialised to the material they are handling. This is certainly the case for the transport of bulk cement, china clay, crushed stone, coal, oil, steel, fly-ash and some manufactured items like cars.

In recent years, specialised fixed formation trains have also been used in the UK, known as freightliners, which run on regular routes from ports and various factories carrying standard containers.

Some of the larger dedicated bulk carrying vehicles that run in the UK have twin wheeled bogies and a total 'all-up' laden weight of up to 100 tons. This has the effect of producing a train which imposes 25 ton axle loadings down the full length of the train. This is very punishing to the supporting track and structures and must be taken into account by all engineers engaged both in vehicle and bridge design.

3.14 Specialised engineering rolling stock

Railways were originally very labour intensive. This applied particularly to the civil engineering activities involved in both laying and maintaining the permanent way and its supporting earthworks.

Fig. 3.13. Ballast tamping machine

Early etchings of railway building activities show that a great deal was achieved by sheer weight of manpower assisted only by hand tools, wheelbarrows and the trusty horse. Contractors often laid temporary track on which they used their own small steam locomotives hauling simple wagons. On these tracks some used simple steam powered mobile cranes but that was about the limit of mechanical plant available.

On railways today engineers have designed many items of plant, both stationary and mobile, which reduce considerably the manual tasks associated with keeping the track up to a good standard.

All specialised engineering rolling stock has to comply with all the safety, signalling and operational requirements on the railway. Some are self propelled and can be treated as a train operating in its own right. Other plant is hauled to site as part of a train and only operated under its own power within the confines of a complete possession of the railway.

Specialised vehicles included the following:

- Ballast Tamping Machines
- Ballast Cleaners
- Ballast Hopper Wagons
- Stone Blowers
- Mobile Rail Cranes
- Long Welded Rail Cars
- Cleaning Trains
- Inspection cars/trolleys
- Snow and Leaf clearing vehicles
- Concreting trains
- Drain/sump cleaners.
- Battery cars/Ballast locomotives
- Tunnel cleaners
- Platelayers' trolleys
- Personnel carriers
- Track Recording Cars
- Rail Grinders
- Special flat cars/bolster wagons for track

3.15 Manufacturing methods

Originally railway rolling stock was manufactured using simple engineering skills with most components being 'bespoke'. Manufacture was labour intensive which was relatively cheap. In more recent years multiple engineering skills have become involved with more specialisation, complex design and use of standard components. Skilled labour has become progressively more expensive in real terms. Additionally there have been a number of major changes in manufacturing technology. These changes include the following:

- Riveting has been replaced by welding
- There is an increase in the use of aluminium and stainless steel
- Plastics have been introduced
- There is a greater use of jigs and fixtures
- Computerised manufacture and production control
- Introduction of Quality Assurance

CHAPTER 4

Depots and Workshops

4.1 Proper maintenance of rolling stock

Any railway relies upon proper maintenance of both its rolling stock and its infrastructure to ensure that efficient and reliable operation is sustained.

Both operational and maintenance considerations need to be fully taken into account at the planning stage and should be monitored in the first years of operation to check that assumptions were correct and procedures are adequate. Failure to do this could result in a steadily declining standard of satisfaction.

Designers and engineers must discipline themselves to revisit installations or systems to see for themselves how things have actually worked out in practice. This is common sense but the need to do this cannot be over stressed and applies to all disciplines. The author has visited many railway systems around the world and could cite examples where consultants have repeated mistakes on new railways simply because they did not check experience gained on other similar installations. Similarly, all those engaged in design in any field need to consult and draw on the 'real life' experience of manufacturers, operators and maintainers.

There are many examples of this but just one is given. Deficient sliding door gear is one of the most frequent reasons for taking rapid transit stock out of service. Designers need to understand in this area for instance what usually causes the failures and how often they occur, how passengers' action contributes to the failures, what the operators have to do to rectify matters in the immediate term and how quickly faults can be rectified.

Apart from the obvious economic considerations, lack or deterioration of adequate maintenance of rolling stock will have a progressively adverse effect on the following:

- Safety
- Customer satisfaction and co-operation
- Customer perception of reliability
- Availability — this will influence the total number of trains that are necessary in the fleet for a given level of service
- Morale and 'pride' of operating staff

4.2 Rolling stock maintenance considerations

Generally speaking, maintenance of rolling stock can be divided into two main categories, planned and unplanned or more usually known as routine and casualty. In the area of planned routine maintenance activity the following can be included:

- Preparation for service
- Routine examination
- Cleaning
- Renewal of consumables (such as brake pads, light bulbs, upholstery cushions etc)
- unit exchange
- major mechanical overhaul

In the routine completion of all these activities, operators and engineers need to co-operate to establish the best layout, sequence of events and frequency for every activity involved.

4.3 Establishing a maintenance regime

Every railway needs to establish for itself a regime for the regular maintenance of rolling stock. The various activities, involving both inspection and work to components, will necessitate some time when stock is not available for normal operation. It is difficult to get the balance right between over and under maintenance and this must be watched carefully, allowing suitable adjustments to be made in both procedures and frequencies when these are shown to be necessary.

With a new railway, or with entirely new stock on an existing railway, the following factors should be taken into consideration when establishing a maintenance regime initially:

- experience with similar stock on other railways,
- manufacturers recommendations,
- theoretical wear and fatigue deterioration of replaceable components e.g., brake linings etc,
- climatic conditions i.e., extremes of heat, cold, or wet,
- degree of heavy use e.g., extreme crowding of passengers or carriage of very heavy and abrasive materials,
- required comfort/cleanliness standards for passengers concerned e.g., First Class overnight long distance travellers would expect a higher standard than short distance suburban Standard Class commuters, perhaps.

It is essential that all those involved in maintenance are provided with reliable and up to date information. Staff need to be adequately trained and be provided with the necessary maintenance manuals. Of equal importance is the necessity to keep accurate up to date records of every maintenance activity on each item of rolling stock so that the full history of each vehicle is properly documented. In the past this activity was a laborious but necessary 'chore', but with the advent of the computer the keeping of such records should be much easier.

4.4 Maintenance management

Having established a maintenance regime each railway system will need to set up an organisation for adequately managing the maintenance process and monitoring it. Up until very recent years it has been traditional on most railways to maintain rolling stock 'in-house'. This involved extensive workshops and proportionately large labour forces but it did have the effect of keeping control within the parent organisation. In this case however, the size of the workforce and the workshop plant and facilities needs to carefully match the actual demand or it will be inadequate if too small or unduly costly if too extensive. Manpower can be adjusted if demand changes but it is not always possible to modify plant and buildings once they have been installed.

In recent years, much more thought has been given to contracting out certain maintenance operations. This is more flexible if demand changes but does require more control. Many components and units are now made for easy replacement. The replacement of the units can be done in the railway's own workshops or depots leaving the manufacturers to service or repair their own units and components on a contractual basis. Because of this trend, many railway workshops have either closed or become very much reduced in size.

4.5 The balance between workshops and depots

Originally railway companies set up both railway workshops and railway depots on their systems. As practically all the engineering work was done 'in-house', the scope of activities was very wide and depots and workshops had very differing functions.

In many cases, the early railway companies manufactured their own locomotives and rolling stock and carried out all major repairs and refitting in the same works. The practice has gradually changed over the years and now most manufacture and major overhaul is carried out by independent suppliers.

Railways therefore need to carefully consider what engineering activities still need to be carried out on their own premises and by their own staff. Having decided this, it is a short step to a decision as to what operations are most sensibly carried out at a depot and which are better done at a separate workshop location.

On many railways, depots contain a minimum of workshop facilities for day-to-day maintenance and unit/component changing, the major work being carried out elsewhere by tendered contract, either by supplier or 'in-house'.

Fig. 4.1. Diesel-electric maintenance depot.

4.6 Depot siting

The siting of depots on any railway system is important and needs to be given careful consideration in the planning stage.

Main line railway operating patterns usually require depots to be as close as possible to termini or to origin/destination points for freight running. There will often be severe constraints at such locations relating to space availability and high land costs. Even so, final locations should be not too far away from the ideal siting as 'empty running' costs and times will amount to a considerable sum over a depot lifetime.

Some reduction of these costs can sometimes be effected by stabling trains in sidings or even station platforms closer to the point of operational origin than depots. However this can have disadvantages in that rolling stock will not have full depot facilities available should cleaning, minor overnight servicing or repairs be necessary.

Metros and light railways which serve a city or large conurbation will often have lines or services which originate in outer suburbs, run through the city centre and out to suburbs on the other side, with some converging or at least interchange with other lines or transport modes.

At the beginning and end of the traffic day on such systems traffic demand will fall off, particularly in the outer areas. Because of this some trains will often be reversed before they reach the outer termini, reducing the train frequency in the outer suburbs. This likely pattern of operation needs to be carefully considered before location of depots is finalised on Metros, light railways and other essentially suburban commuter services.

Fig. 4.2. Typical Metro Depot for London Underground.

For Metros therefore the most practical location for a depot is often about half to three quarters of the distance out from the city centre. At this point land will be more available, but not too far out for easy access for operating and engineering staff.

At this location, it is also more likely that the potential problems of lack of space, noise, pollution and proximity of neighbours can be overcome.

Another advantage of such a location is that the depot can be double ended. This means that entry and exit to the depot for trains leaving or entering service can be in either direction and at either end. Experience has shown that if a depot has just one point of entry from the running lines, extensive delays and disruption can be caused by just one train becoming immobilised or one set of points failing at the depot entrance. In bad weather also frozen points at one end can completely shut up all the trains in a depot at the commencement of a traffic day.

Fig. 4.3. DLR depot during construction.

4.7 The needs of the maintainer

Maintenance requirements need to be carefully considered by the designer of rolling stock. All too often stock is designed without any proper appreciation of the needs of the maintainer.

As a guide, the following twelve key requirements must be kept in mind:

1. Good access to components
2. No dust or dirt traps
3. Simple fault finding systems

4. No superfluous equipment
5. High reliability, proven equipment
6. Minimum number of quick release fastenings
7. Easily removable sub-assemblies
8. Small number of tools required
9. Simple isolation of systems
10. All fixings capable of torque tightening
11. Equipment cases watertight
12. Maximum interchangeability of components

As can be seen, a few moments consideration will show that all these requirements are simply 'common sense'. It is surprising however how often maintainers are thwarted in carrying out simple operations because one of these considerations has been overlooked.

4.8 Basic requirements for depots

Each railway must carefully look at the different functions that need to be carried out within the depot. The size of the fleet, diversity of stock type and turn-around of trains will all have a bearing on the facilities required.

The following twelve basic general requirements need to be addressed:

1. Sidings which are adequate to stable the maximum number of trains/units likely to be in the depot, with adequate access walkways for operating and engineering staff.
2. Adequate provision of point and crossing work and 'shunt necks' to enable trains to be moved within the depot to allow proper cleaning and maintenance and marshalling in correct order for service. The layout should preferably be 'double ended'. Some form of control of points and train movements in the depot needs to be provided.
3. Covered workshops with all necessary cranes/jacks, inspection pits, walkways, equipment, test facilities and etc for maintenance work and lifting. Road access needs to be provided to the workshop area adequate to handle the largest components that will need to be taken away for major overhaul or replacement.

4. Adequate lighting and heating as appropriate.
5. Staff facilities, offices and training rooms.
6. Stores with both road and rail access.
7. Wheel turning facility.
8. Raised bogie roads and bogie wash.
9. Repair facility for painted surfaces.
10. Train washing arrangements for both internal and external surfaces and underframes. Specially constructed wash roads are necessary to enable used water to be properly collected, filtered and channelled away to drains.
11. De-icing arrangements.
12. Fire alarms and protection.

Fig. 4.4. Train washing machine.

In applying these requirements to any railway system it is advisable to remember that as well as the normal planned and predictable maintenance items of work, there will always also be unforeseen emergency items which will demand urgent work from time to time. If there is no spare capacity in depots, such incidents could cause major disruption to regular maintenance work.

Collision damage may occur from time to time. Also a small amount of local damage might occur to a large number of trains originating from a track or structure irregularity. A good example of this would be damage to wheels through sliding on wet leaves or damage to collector gear due to a displaced current rail ramp or walkway board.

On electrified railways, there may well be other specialised requirements that will need to be provided in railway depots. This will probably include inspection and maintenance of current collection equipment and possibly battery charging and storing.

4.9 Performance indicators and audit

It is necessary to establish reliable performance indicators for all classes of rolling stock to ensure that engineers and operators can detect any deterioration in maintenance standards. There must be a continuous search for the optimum maintenance regime that will give the most economic performance overall. It is also essential that a periodic audit is carried out to check independently that standards are being maintained.

CHAPTER 5

Track

5.1 The origin and development of railway track

Before the beginning of the eighteenth century, wheeled transport was generally hauled by horse and ran on surfaces which at the best was reinforced by a broken stone foundation and at the worst was simply a mud track. It was found at a very early stage of the development of land transport, that most road surfaces and foundations were very quickly damaged by heavy wagons on rigid wheels.

The first railway tracks were laid down in the eighteenth century for horse drawn trains of wagons in collieries and quarries. These 'hauling ways' initially had a surface of stone slabs or timber baulks which proved unsatisfactory as loads grew heavier. As the Industrial Revolution progressed, the idea was developed further by adding wrought iron plates to reduce wear on the wooden baulks. This evolved further first to cast iron plates and later to edge rails, enabling for the first time the use of flanged iron wheels.

By the time locomotives came on the scene in the early nineteenth century, wrought iron rails had developed further and became strong enough to support these heavy engines without assistance from longitudinal timbers.

In 1825, the Stockton and Darlington Railway was constructed adopting track of wrought iron rails resting in cast iron chairs supported on stone blocks set in the ground at three feet intervals. The rails were of 'T' section 15 feet long and weighed about 28 lbs per yard.

Fig. 5.1. Bullhead Section Rail.

As experience was gained and new technology evolved, rails steadily increased in size, both in length and cross section, and were made in steel rather than iron. Early railways evolved the 'bullhead' or dumbbell section of rail which was standard throughout the UK up to the Second World War. This rail was manufactured in increasing lengths and heavier sections and by the early 1900's had been generally standardised to 60 foot lengths and about 95 lbs per yard weight. Most railways today use flat-bottomed rail.

The individual stone block sleepers were early found to be unwieldy and unsatisfactory from several points of view, largely relating to weight and the lack of tying of rails at a fixed gauge. These blocks were quickly replaced by timber cross sleepers which proved to be much more economic and satisfactory. Cross sleepers, or 'ties' as they are known in some countries, have been generally adopted world-wide and are now often manufactured in concrete or steel although timber is still used extensively. At a very early stage, the need for good preservation of softwood left in wet ballast became very obvious. By the 1880's, several railway companies had set up their own plants to impregnate sleepers with creosote under pressure.

5.2 Basic components of track

Today most railways have rolling stock with hard steel flanged wheels running on two rails set at or about 1432 mm standard gauge, supported in some way to spread loads to the ground below.

'Sub-grade' is the term used for the natural soil stratum, or embankment soil, after trimming off organic topsoil and made ground, upon which the track bed is constructed.

The 'Trackbed' comprises the ballast and any sub-ballast layers and is there to support the track, to drain water from the bottom of the sleepers and to distribute the imposed track load to such a degree that the sub-grade can resist the imposed bearing pressure adequately.

5.3 Track ballast

Early railway engineers did not at first realise the important engineering function carried out by the ballast, as outlined above. Because of this all manner of material was used beneath the sleepers which today would be considered completely unsuitable. This included materials which would be cheaply and easily available locally such as ashes, chalk and clay.

Experience soon showed that good quality ballast, made of well graded gravel, crushed gravel, limestone or igneous rock was necessary if adequate foundation and good drainage is to be achieved for a reasonable period.

Today, the required depth of good quality ballast beneath sleepers varies depending upon the maximum speed of trains, the maximum axle loads carried and the gross annual tonnage expected. In general, the absolute minimum depth of ballast needed beneath sleepers for even a lightly loaded railway should never be less than 150 mm and heavily loaded main lines can require as much as 280 mm. The currently recommended minimum thicknesses of ballast beneath sleepers for lines in the UK are as shown in Fig. 5.2 below.

To ensure both lateral and longitudinal stability of the track, particularly when using continuously welded rail, it is essential that ballast is taken up to the level of the top of the sleepers between the sleepers and given a good 'shoulder' at the sleeper ends.

Line Speed (km/h)	Line Tonnage (tonnes/yr)	Ballast Depth (mm)
Up to 200	Over 7 million	280
	Under 7 million	230
Up to 170	Over 15 million	280
	Under 15 million	230
Less than 130	no limit	150

Fig. 5.2. Recommended ballast depths.

5.4 Materials for track ballast

Good quality track ballast is made from crushed natural rock with particles not larger than 50 mm or generally smaller than 28 mm. Angular stones are preferable to naturally rounded stones, to achieve the best interlock properties and resistance to longitudinal and lateral movement under dynamic loading. If ballast particles are larger than the maximum size stated, there may only be two or three stones between the underside of the sleeper and the subgrade will be insufficient to properly distribute the load. Too many small stones below 28 mm will however clog the ballast and reduce, in the longer term, its drainage properties. Samples of track ballast must be checked for grading by sieve analysis. Not more than 3% by weight should be retained on the 50 mm square mesh sieve and not more than 2% should pass through the 28 mm sieve.

Ballast particles can suffer degradation due to the action of traffic and maintenance operations in broadly two ways. Either edges can become rounded and lose their interlocking effect or particles can break or crush under repeated loading. Some of the softer stones suffer badly from attrition in the presence of water. This deterioration, particularly at rail joints, can be associated with 'wet spots' in the track which can cause rapid deterioration of line, level and riding comfort.

Certain tests can be introduced to check the wet attrition qualities of ballast. Generally speaking, limestones tend to have poor wet attrition qualities, crushed granite being one of the best, although expensive.

5.5 Sleeper functions

Sleepers and bearers or timbers (for points and crossings) need to fulfil the following basic functions:

1. Spread wheel loads to ballast
2. Hold rails to gauge and inclination
3. Transmit lateral and longitudinal forces
4. Insulate rails electrically
5. Provide a base for rail seats and fastenings

Sleepers are also often called upon to fulfil other secondary but important functions which should not be overlooked. These include:

1. Supporting wheels and/or jacks direct (in a derailment situation)
2. Acting as transverse beams when sitting on temporary 'waybeams'
3. Supporting signal engineering and other safety related equipment (such as trip cocks and point motors)
4. Supporting conductor rails, electrical bonds and feeder cables
5. Reducing noise and vibration on non-ballasted bridge decks

5.6 Timber sleepers

The traditional timber sleeper was accepted by most railways as standard up to about the middle of the twentieth century, although its durability limitations were recognised.

Even today there are still many railways using timber sleepers, where the advantages of good resilience, ease of handling, adaptability to non-standard situations or electrical insulation are very important.

Timber sleepers and bearers for surface railways are usually made of softwood, either imported Douglas Fir or homegrown Scots Pine. The

Fig. 5.3. Individual renewal of Timber Sleepers on LUL.

standard dimensions for softwood sleepers used in the UK are 254 mm. wide by 127 mm. thick in cross-section by 2600 mm. long.

All softwoods used in sleepers and bearers must be thoroughly seasoned and then impregnated under pressure with a suitable preservative before use. Traditionally, this preservative has been hot creosote but other materials have been used successfully in recent years which may have less associated health hazards.

Main line surface railways are now progressively converting their important lines to prestressed concrete sleepers, which are described later.

All lines in deep tube tunnels or in locations where fire could be a risk, are provided with sleepers and pitblocks made from imported untreated hardwood such as Jarrah.

Jarrah timbers used on the surface for points and crossing work which is not protected from the weather can last up to 35 years. In the protected environment of dry tube tunnels, Jarrah sleepers on the London Underground have been known to last in excess of 50 years before needing renewal.

The author has in his possession a handsome polished jarrah pen and pencil box which bears the following interesting inscription under the lid:

> 'This box is made from jarrah sleepers withdrawn from the London Tube railways after 54 years continuous service. It is estimated that during this time 500 million passengers travelled over the sleepers.'

Such comment speaks for itself. Hardwood sleepers eventually usually need replacing after this long period not because the general condition of the timber has deteriorated but because it is by then not possible to get a sound fixing for chair screws.

Softwood treated sleepers on the surface can be expected to last between 15 and 25 years depending on location and traffic use. Renewal is usually required because bad splitting and/or rot has occurred.

5.7 Prestressed concrete sleepers (Monobloc)

As a substitute to softwood, some experimental work was carried out during the late 1930's on concrete sleepers. Originally, ordinary reinforced concrete was used but not found very satisfactory for a number of reasons. At that stage, concrete simply replaced timber, bullhead rails and cast iron chairs being used as in other conventional track.

After the Second World War, prestressed concrete was developed and used extensively on new structures. The great advantage of prestressed concrete was that concrete is kept under compression under all conditions of flexure, both under load and after. This means that tension cracks do not occur which can allow ingress of moisture and corrosion of embedded steel.

Development of prestressed sleepers took place about the same time as development of flat bottomed rail and direct fastenings.

At the time of writing, the standard sleeper for main line railways in the UK is the F27(ASorBS) prestressed concrete sleeper manufactured by the pretensioned method. In this method, the prestressing tendons are tensioned prior to the concrete being placed and are only released once the concrete has reached sufficient compressive strength to resist the induced forces thus applied. This method is also sometimes referred to as the 'Long Line' system, as sleepers are cast in long lines or beds of twenty five sleepers or more.

Some counties outside the UK adopt the post-tensioning method where tendons are placed in debonding sheaths and the stress is applied after the concrete has hardened by application of tensile force to the tendons by jacking and final anchoring. This method is slower but less capital intensive and lends itself to small-scale production and situations where demand is less.

Standard prestressed concrete sleepers used in the UK are normally 2515 mm long by 264 mm wide. The depth varies from 203 mm at the rail seat to 165 mm at the centre line giving a total weight of 285 kg. The prestress is provided by 6 No. 9.3 mm strands for standard use increased to 8 No. strands for heavy duty. These sleepers are capable of sustaining an equivalent dynamic load of 24 tonnes at each rail seat. Allowing for impact, lurching, wheel flats, poor rail joints and etc this is equivalent to the effects of the passage of a static 25 tonnes axle.

Fig. 5.4. Standard prestressed concrete sleepers.

Metros and light rail systems have extensively also adopted prestressed concrete sleepers. Where maximum axle loads are less than for main line as shown above, the sleeper dimensions may be reduced accordingly. However, great care must be taken in the design to ensure that adequate allowance is made for dynamic effects, particularly for both 'hogging' and 'sagging' bending moments.

The main disadvantage of the concrete sleeper over its timber predecessor is that of weight. Timber sleepers were often manhandled into their final position and replacement of single defective sleepers (or 'spotting' as it is sometimes known) was also done by hand. With concrete sleepers, some form of mechanisation is required for these operations.

5.8 Twin block sleepers

The twin block sleeper consists of two reinforced concrete blocks joined together with a steel tie bar cast into the blocks. This type of sleeper is used extensively in Europe, particularly in France, but not in the UK. The standard sleeper weighs 230 kg which is less than the monobloc equivalent. However handling and placing can be difficult due to the tendency to twist when lifted. Twinblock sleepers can be provided with resilient 'boots' and can be incorporated into non-ballasted slab track or monolithic embedment in road surfaces for light rail street running.

5.9 Steel sleepers

Steel sleepers have been hardly ever used in the UK, largely because of cost and fear of corrosion in our variable weather conditions.

However, there are countries throughout the world where these sleepers are used successfully, particularly where trains run at moderate speeds only. Reference should be made to BS 500. Most steel sleepers are inverted troughs which are either rolled to that section or rolled flat and then hot pressed to the trough shape.

Being only 68 kg in weight, these sleepers are easy to handle but the inverted trough makes them difficult to satisfactorily pack with ballast.

They have been shown to be completely satisfactory however in sidings and depots. Electrical insulation is necessary at fastenings if track circuits are being used for train detection and this is not always a simple or effective matter.

In some climates, the normal coating of millscale and rust is sufficient to protect against significant loss of section by corrosion. Sleepers can however be given protection by dipping in bitumen or oil during the production process.

5.10 Rail fastenings, baseplates and pads

Early railways adopted various forms of cast iron chair which were fixed to the sleepers and in which rails sat, being held in position by hardwood wedges or 'keys'. All railways which used bullhead section rail used fixings which were basically of this type. With the introduction of flat-bottomed rail starting in the late 1940's, a new form of fastening had to evolve.

Fig. 5.5. Flat-Bottom (FB) rail.

The need was to design a resilient connection between rail and sleeper capable of resisting all forces induced by the passage of trains and by temperature and weather variations over a long period of time.

It was soon found that too rigid fixings became loose under vibration and that some degree of elasticity was necessary to resist both creep and buckling. Maintenance of the clip clamping force on the rail foot or 'toe load' was soon realised as being of crucial importance in this respect.

Since the 1940's many FB rail resilient fasteners have been designed, manufactured and used throughout the world, with varying degrees of success.

These fastenings can be grouped into three distinctive types.

These types are as follows:

- An elastic rail spike. This is driven into pre-drilled holes in sleepers and can be used with or without a steel or cast iron base plate.
- A spring clip bearing on the foot of the rail held down by a nut and bolt element tightened to a predetermined torque. This type of fastening is still used widely in France and Germany
- A spring clip driven into a hole or slot in a 'shoulder' either cast into the sleeper or part of a base plate. The act of driving in the clip either twists or bends the clip thus creating a toe load on the rail.

In the UK in recent years most railways, both main line and metro as well as some light railways, have gone for the last type when using FB rail.

The standard fastening used by British Rail on all new FB track in recent years has been the Pandrol clip. This clip is made from circular section spring steel bar by a process which involves heating the bar, hot pressing into shape and then quenching and annealing. The majority of plain line track on BR is laid on concrete sleepers without base plates and in this case the anchorage shoulder is cast into the sleeper during manufacture.

Where Pandrol rail clips are used in conjunction with base plates the latter are secured to the timber or sleeper by chair screws.

Where DC electrified railways have conductor rails running close to running rails, it is necessary to ensure that rail clips can be placed and maintained without potential damage or dislocation of the conductor rails. With the Pandrol clip, this condition is satisfied as the clip is introduced into the shoulder and driven in a direction parallel to the running rail.

Some earlier spring clips were driven at right angles to the rail which certainly would not be possible close to conductor rails.

Fastenings require insulation both from electrical current and from vibration/noise. This is achieved by the introduction of resilient insulating pads at points of contact.

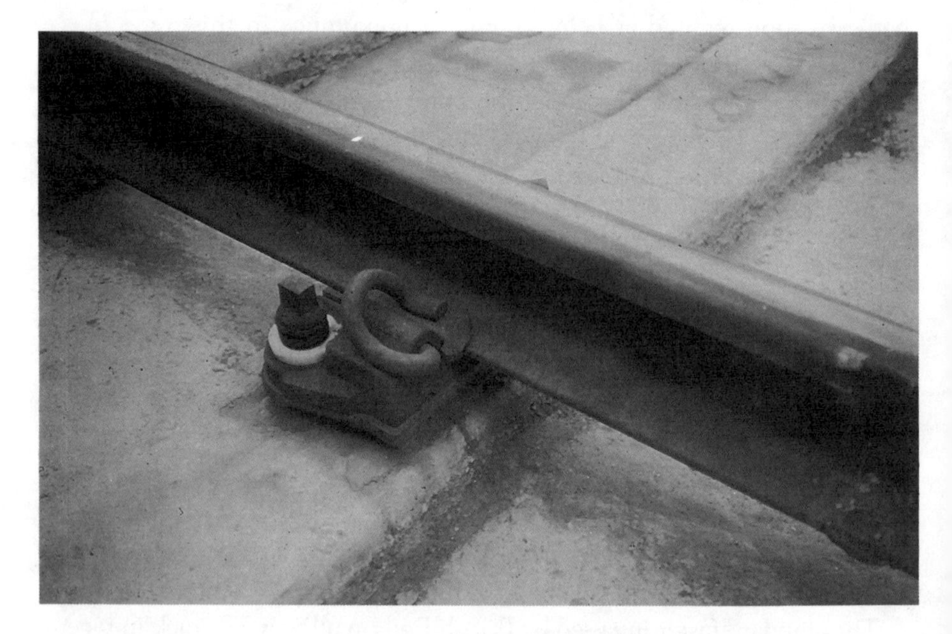

Fig. 5.6. The Pandrol Clip.

5.11 Rails

All modern railways use steel rails which are specifically rolled for the purpose from steel which has the required qualities of strength, fatigue endurance and wear and corrosion resistance. This type of steel is fully covered by British Standard Specification 11.

As has been mentioned previously, the shape of the rail has now become generally standardised as the Flat-Bottom (FB) rail. This is sometimes known as the Vignoles rail, after the inventor. British Rail have now standardised on the BS113A section rail for all important lines.

The head of the rail has an almost flat top with curves at the outer edges designed to fit the shape of the wheel tyre. One of the features of a well matched rail head and wheel tyre is that, when the axis of the wheel set coincides with the longitudinal axis of the track and the rail is set at its correct inclination of 1 in 20 to the vertical, the point of contact between the two is very close to the centre line of the rail. This is very desirable since it minimises the twisting effect on the rail which an eccentrically applied wheel load would produce, and by keeping the contact area away from the gauge corner, reduces both corner 'shelling' and fatigue damage.

The rail head sides slope at 1 in 20. This is to compensate for the 1 in 20 inwards slope of the rails and not only makes it simpler to check the gauge but ensures that when side wear takes place the associated gauge widening is minimised.

The thick web of the BS113A section is designed to give the rail adequate shear strength to guard against fatigue failures, particularly around fishbolt holes and under heavy axle loads at joints.

The foot of the rail is broad enough to give stability against roll-over, remembering that steering forces exerted by rolling stock produce torsional and lateral forces which have to be resisted by the rail and transmitted via the fastenings to the sleeper.

In addition to the primary function, the rail has secondary functions relating to the carrying of track circuit currents and in some cases on electrified railways, conveying return traction currents.

Each section of rail that is used requires special steel castings, clips, bolts, resilient pads, fishplates, expansion switches etc. to make up the full structural system of the track. Most railway authorities endeavour to keep rail types and sizes to a minimum to ensure also that maintenance stocks of replacement components can also be kept to a sensible minimum. A great deal of capital can be tied up in stock which is kept in stores just to cover an eventuality which may never happen.

There are also a number of signal related track components, like block joints, which are incorporated into the track structural system.

With third and fourth rail DC electrification systems, there are also a large number of insulators and other fittings relating to the track which are required.

5.12 Rail wear

Abrasive wear occurs when there is contact between the side of the flange of a wheel and the gauge face of the rail. This contact usually takes place between the leading outer wheel of a vehicle bogey and the outer rail of a curve.

On curves, careful periodic check must be carried out of the outer rail to ensure that side wear is kept within prescribed limits. Failure to do this could result in a derailment.

Where curves are tighter than 200 m radius, continuous check rails should be provided inside the inner rail. This check rail is to be set not more than about 50 mm inside the running rail or at a distance that will ensure that the inside face of the flange of the inner wheels will bear on the check rail thus sharing the centrifugal force between the check rail and the outer rail through flange bearing.

Abrasive wear of rails can be reduced by the use of rail lubricators placed at strategic positions. Great care needs to be exercised in the use of lubricators to ensure that only flanges are lubricated. Lubricant deposited on the top of rail heads can cause problems with braking, acceleration and wheel-spin. This is particularly important where trains are automatically driven or where stopping positions are critical such as when rolling stock doors have to line up with platform doors.

When wheels run along fairly straight track with flanges just clear of the rails, the contact area between wheel and rail is extremely small. In theory the contact would only be a point which would make contact pressures infinitely high. In practice both surfaces deform slightly to give a contact 'patch'. Even so typically such a patch has only an area of about 100 mm^2. under the heaviest wheel load. This gives pressures as high as 1200 N/mm^2 which is higher than the yield point of the steel. This has the effect of causing the contact patch to become plastic and to flow causing various wear patterns and irregularities over time.

Where rails become side worn near to limit on curves, extra life can be obtained by either turning the high rail on jointed track or transposing the two rails on continuously welded rail. Close inspection of the existing inner rail outer edge must be carried out before transposing to ensure that there are no other defects present such as roll-over, 'lipping' or plastic flow that would make the ride rough and precipitate failure of the new running edge. If speeds in excess of 120 km/h (75 miles/h) are expected transposing should only be carried out if reprofiling of the existing inner rail is carried out.

Wear on point and crossings needs to be carefully watched on a regular basis. Some repair of bad wear can be done by welding but in most cases components need to be changed.

In jointed track, excessive wear often takes place at rail joints or fishbolt holes and is the main reason for rerailing. Joints also increase wear on rolling stock. This is one of the main reasons why main line railways are progressively changing to continuously welded rails.

When a derailment occurs on any railway at any location, rail wear must be fully investigated as this can often prove to be the root cause. All rails should be closely inspected including any tell-tale signs of where wheels ran at the time of the derailment.

5.13 The desirability of removing rail joints

The earliest memories of many from childhood days relate to the 'Clackerty-clack' of steam railways.

In those days every schoolboy knew that rails were sixty foot long and had to have fairly loose bolted joints so that the rails could expand in the hot weather and contract in the cold. Well understood also to the regular suburban commuter was the familiar sight from the carriage window of the platelayer driving in keys and greasing fishbolts.

To many career railway men however these 'chores' represented a sizeable annual workload and removal of joints, if it could be done practically and safely, would be a giant leap forward. Apart from the reduction of potential track irregularities and smoothing and quietening down of the ride, removal of rail joints would clearly show a reduction of wear on wheels and rolling stock components in general. There would also be an improvement in the performance of underframe and bogie components subject to fatigue.

Up to the outbreak of the Second World War in 1939, mechanical, civil, structural and marine engineers had all used bolting and rivetting as the main method of joining together steelwork in its various forms.

During the War, metal arc welding began to be used for the first time and after the War welding began to be used extensively, particularly in structures, machines and ships.

5.14 Introduction of track welding

In the immediate post-war years, certain wartime teething troubles with metal arc welding were eventually ironed out and better understood, as wider experience was gained. In particular, failure of welds or the parent metal in the heat affected zone of welds by metal fatigue took some time to understand and correctly predict. These fatigue failures were particularly troublesome in some of the early welded ships and to a lesser extent in some welded bridge members.

Metal arc welding was used extensively on steel structures in shop fabrication. By the late fifties, shop welding of this type had completely replaced the earlier shop rivetting of structures, site joints generally being site bolted or very infrequently, site welded.

Although some metal arc welding and electroslag welding is used for the fabrication and repair of point and crossing work, the welding of rails end to end to form continuous welded rail (CWR) is carried out in the shops by a process known as Flash Butt Welding (FBW).

Flash butt welding of rails commenced in the UK on a large scale in the late 1950's and since that time, the process has been refined and improved but still remains basically the same. In the mid 1950's, London Transport introduced flash butt long welded rails using the standard bullhead section. The FBW rails were produced by welding five standard sixty foot lengths into a long rail of 300 ft (about 90 m). These rails were joined using 'tight' bolted joints where the fishplates were clamped to the rail using high strength friction grip bolts, tightened to a predetermined torque. London Transport (LUL) are now in the process of changing over to flat-bottom rail.

Main line railways in the UK use flat bottom section rail for CWR which is flash butt welded in the shops in lengths up to 240 m. In recent years in the UK British Steel PLC have been able to supply long lengths of rail already flash butt welded into long lengths.

5.15 Shop welding to produce long rails

The process of Flash Butt Welding is used in the shops to join rails which are later to be incorporated into Continuous Welded Rail sites. This process involves clamping the rails at a predetermined gap distance and passing a high current across the gap at a low voltage, during which the work pieces are brought together.

Electrical resistance heating first causes contacting surface irregularities to melt and subsequently raises the temperature of the whole interface to near melting point. Once the components are sufficiently heated they are forged together, and excess molten steel at the interface is forced out of the weld area.

The stages of FBW in the shops include burn off, preheating, flashing, forging and post weld treatment.

Once the weld has solidified, integral shears at the welding plant remove the excess upset from the periphery of the weld, leaving about 1 mm proud all round the weld section.

The welds are then straightened and the railhead ground to give a smooth profile for the weld along the length on the rail.

Unlike metal arc welding, no electrodes or added metal is used, only the parent metal is fused. Because some of the metal at the rail ends is forced out of the section profile, the overall effective length of the rail reduces by about 20 mm for each weld.

5.16 Site welding to produce CWR

On arrival at site, long rails are welded to form CWR using the Thermit or alumino thermic welding process. This method, which was discovered in 1896 by Hans Goldmidt, is based on the reduction of heavy metal oxides by aluminium. Thermit welding was first used in Hungary in 1904 and most of Europe had adopted the process for site rail joints by the late 1920's. The process was not used very widely in the UK however until the 1950's.

Some light railways have used Thermit welding of short rails throughout without the use of FBW into long rails beforehand. Although this is cheaper and removes the need for a shop process, the practice is not recommended for railways carrying heavy axle loads.

Thermit welds are completely satisfactory but have less consistency than FBW, being carried out in the open on site rather than in controlled workshop conditions.

Annual statistics, published on reported broken rails at welds in the UK over recent years, strongly bear out the better performance of FBW in practice.

In this process, the rails to be joined are set in position, fixed in their baseplates, with the ends properly aligned and with a gap of 22–26 mm between them. A refractory mould is then placed around the joint and a thermit portion is ignited in a refractory crucible above the mould. The portion is a combination of powders which after reaction will produce a weld metal which matches the chemistry and metallurgy of the parent rails. When the reaction is complete, the crucible is tapped and steel pours into the moulds to form the weld. Slag, being less dense than the steel, remains at the top of the mould. The weld is allowed to cool after which the excess metal, mould material and slag is trimmed away and the joint is ground to profile.

Fig. 5.7. Continuous Welded Track.

5.17 Stressing or 'Locking-up' of CWR

With jointed short rails, the object is to allow rails to expand and contract during extremes of temperature to avoid the build up of compressive and tensile stresses.

In long welded rails and CWR however, the rail is constrained so that it cannot expand or contract. In this case, in order that the rail shall remain at its original length, the rail undergoes compressive and tensile strain, which is equal and opposite to thermal strain.

By simple calculation using Hooke's Law, (F = strain × A × E), it can be seen that a restrained standard BS113A FB rail increased in temperature by say 45°C will produce a force of 76.5 tonnes in the rail.

A compressive force of such magnitude in hot weather is sufficient to cause a buckle of the track and it is essential for safety that development of such a force is prevented. Similarly, high tensile forces in extremely cold weather can cause brittle fracture of rails and must be avoided.

This is done on CWR by artificially extending the rail at the time of installation and fixing it down in a state of tension. The ideal is to fix the rail at a length that it will be, at a temperature that is exactly halfway between the hottest and coldest likely rail temperature. In the UK this is generally accepted as a temperature of 27°C.

The rail may be artificially extended by rail warming or, as is now more usual, by stretching with a tensor.

5.18 Points, switches and crossings

All railways require points or 'turnouts' to be able to divert trains from one track to another and crossings or 'diamonds' to allow trains to cross other tracks at an angle.

This applies to all railways from the most complicated reversible layouts at terminal stations to simple single track tramways with passing loops.

Any assembly of points and crossings is called a layout. Some layouts occur frequently and have acquired their own names. The most common is the 'crossover' which is simply two sets of points laid crossing to crossing in adjoining track enabling trains to change track in one direction. If two crossovers are superimposed, thus enabling movements from either track in either direction, the layout is known as a 'scissors crossover' for obvious reasons. In this layout there are four sets of points and one diamond.

Points or turnouts and diamonds are themselves composed of elements known as crossings and switches.

Fig. 5.8. A crossover layout in BH rail.

5.19 Crossing design and manufacture

A crossing enables a wheel travelling along a given rail to pass through the rail of a track which crosses its path. Where two tracks cross each other at an angle, there are four crossings which make up the resulting diamond. Unless the tracks cross at right angles, there will be two Obtuse Crossings and two at an acute angle known as Common Crossings.

'Built-up' Crossings are manufactured from standard rail and are perhaps the most often seen, having been used traditionally on railways for many decades. In these crossings the four components, the point rail, the splice rail and two wing rails are cut, bent to shape, drilled and machined as necessary and then bolted together as a complete assembly. This type of simple crossing has given good service over many years in countries all round the world. They are subject to wear however, particularly at the tip of the point rail and where the point and splice rail bear against one another. Through bolts also often work loose under traffic.

A 'part-welded' crossing consists essentially of the same four rails as a built-up crossing and is usually made of standard rail. The assembly however is strong enough to take thermal loads and consequently it can be welded into CWR, leaving only the flange way gap as a source of wheel/rail impact. In theory at least, this is a considerable advantage over both built-up crossings and cast crossings, although welding in of components into point and crossing layouts can have a significant time disadvantage when work becomes necessary during possession.

The 'Vee' of a part welded crossing is prepared by machining two pieces of rail into a symmetrical straight splice with a weld preparation milled into the head and foot. The electroslag welding process is used under carefully controlled conditions to produce a continuous homogeneous weld. This welding is laid down automatically with top and bottom welds being done simultaneously to keep any distortion to an absolute minimum. The complete crossing assembly is held together using high strength friction grip bolts tightened to a specified torque or by 'huck' bolts.

Another form of crossing is the cast Austenitic Manganese Steel (or AMS) crossing. In this case there is only one 'monobloc' component making up the entire casting. The casting is made by pouring this special molten steel into a mould which represents the shape of all four components used in the other types of crossing.

This type of crossing is favoured by many railways due to its very high wear resistance and long life. Also due to being monolithic, there is no relative movement of components and the ride is generally very good. Another advantage is the ability to combine more than one crossing in a single casting, as is sometimes the case on a tight scissors crossover.

In spite of its advantages however, AMS crossings do have some disadvantages. Casting as a process is always subject to internal cracking due to cooling and these faults are sometimes difficult to detect before installation.

Also when faults do arise in service, the castings are much heavier and more unwieldy to handle during a limited possession than built-up crossings, particularly in tunnel.

Check rails are provided opposite crossings. Their function is to control the alignment of the wheelset so that it is not possible for the wheel moving across the gap in the throat of the crossing to strike the nose of the crossing or to take a wrong path.

5.20 Points or turnouts

Points or turnouts, as shown below, enable vehicles to be diverted from one track to another and consist of a pair of switches and a crossing, connected by closure rails.

In a set of points the fixed rails on either side are known as stock rails, the moveable rail being known as the switch rail. The switch rail is machined to a sharp tip or toe at one end and the tapered portion of the switch rail is known as the switch tongue. The switch tongue is machined to fit snugly

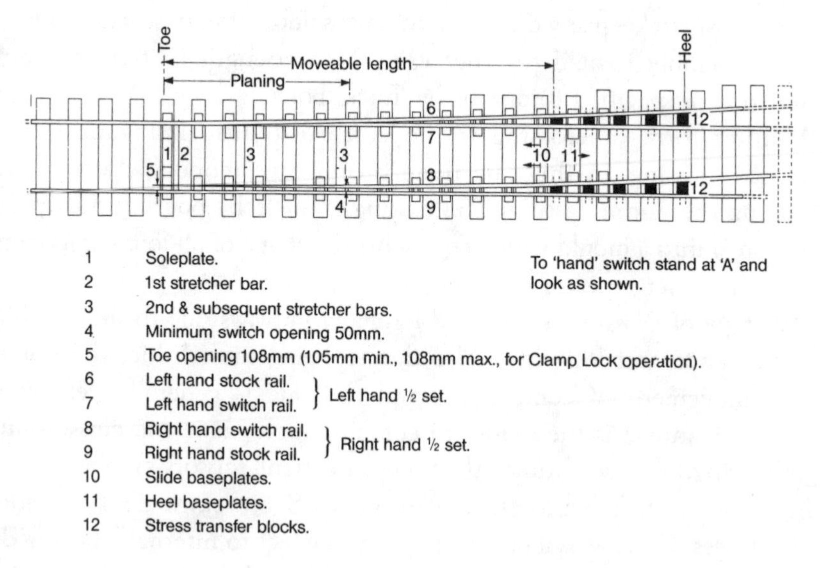

Fig. 5.9. Components of points or turnouts.

into the stock rail in the workshops. It is unwise, when worn to change a stock or switch on its own and both should be changed as a fitting pair. Two movable switches should be held in the correct relative position to each other by at least two stretcher bars.

If the set of points is so arranged that in the predominating traffic direction the tracks diverge, it is known as facing points. If the main traffic direction is such that the two lines merge, they are trailing points.

5.21 Driving, locking and detection of points

In the early days of railways, sets of facing points on passenger lines were avoided because of the high risk of derailment due to wheel flanges 'splitting' stocks and switches. Following this early experience, it became mandatory that all facing points should be locked in position and that the position of each switch should be 'detected' in relation to its mating stock rail.

On modern railways, points are operated by electric or compressed air point motors/machines which operate the points, lock and clamp them in position and also detect whether or not the switches are fully 'home'. There needs to be careful and clear division of responsibility for maintenance and adjustment of all point mechanisms between signal and track engineers.

5.22 Conductor rails and components

Where railways are electrified using either third rail or fourth rail DC systems there are a number of other components and fittings which are track related.

Conductor rails are usually made from steel which is designed to be of high electrical conductivity, containing much less carbon than for normal rails. This means that steel conductor rails are softer and of lower strength than running rails. The rails can be jointed by bolted fishplates or welded.

In recent years, some light rail systems e.g. DLR, have used Aluminium conductor rails for underside contact, with a wearing surface of stainless steel.

Conductor rails are supported by insulators fixed to sleepers at frequencies depending on track curvature, location and type of fixing. The insulator assembly usually consists of a porcelain pot with a cast malleable iron cap having two upstanding 'ears'. These ears locate the conductor rail transversely without restraining longitudinal movement. The insulators are fixed to the sleeper using a pair of wrap round base clips.

At discontinuities and ends of conductor rails, ramps are provided, also supported on sleepers, to pick up and lower collector shoes on rolling stock. It is important that these ramps, which can be welded steel or cast iron are regularly checked to ensure that line and level is correct. Failure to do this can result in damage to rolling stock or track or both.

5.23 Paved concrete track

Paved Concrete Track (sometimes known as PACT) is a continuously reinforced concrete pavement laid by a specially designed 'slip-form' paver. This machine runs on accurately positioned guide rails which ensures that the concrete pavement line and level is very closely controlled. The guide rails are often the long welded rails which will subsequently be repositioned and used as permanent running rails.

The rails are usually supported on baseplates which may have some form of resilience incorporated into their design. Even though the concrete has been accurately positioned, the tolerances achieved may be more than is desirable for accurate positioning of the rails. It is desirable therefore that some adjustment capability is built into the system of final positioning of the baseplates or cast-in fixings. One way of achieving this is for the rails to be finally positioned to line and level on temporary packs/wedges with baseplates and fixing bolts hanging off the rail. Once final rail position is fixed, any gaps at fixing holes and under baseplates can then be grouted up or filled using epoxy mortar.

This track system is much more expensive than conventional ballasted track and cannot be easily modified once laid. It is however of particular use in existing main line size tunnels, where the shallow construction depth may permit the achievement of increased overhead clearances for 25 kV electrification or for the passage of large container trains. In this track system particular attention needs to be given to drainage channels.

5.24 Cast-in precast sleeper track

As a cheaper alternative to PACT, prestressed or reinforced concrete sleepers or special purpose made units can be laid in position accurately with rails fully adjusted and then a concrete slab poured between and around them. In this case, holes through the sleepers are left for transverse reinforcement or some 'hedgehog' starter bars are provided to assist both the precast and *in-situ* elements to act as a whole.

5.25 Floating slab track

In locations where it is vitally important to reduce noise and vibration to an absolute minimum, floating slab track may be considered. It should be stressed that this type of solution is very expensive, requires a lot of space and can only be justified where railways run very close to or under concert halls, churches or operating theatres etc.

In this form of construction the trackform , which may be ballasted or non-ballasted, is supported on a structure which is isolated from the supporting ground by soft resilient bearings.

A notable example of this type of construction is to be found in London under the new Barbican Concert Hall.

5.26 Track installation and renewal

Up to the late 1930's most railways installed or renewed track mainly 'piece-small', using a large amount of skilled labour, only assisted for heavy lifts by rail mounted steam cranes.

In more recent years, special 'purpose-built' equipment has been produced, in particular for surface main lines which mechanizes much of the track laying process. Large machines can now lay panels of sleepered track or place individual sleepers, to be followed by plant laying welded rails in very long lengths.

Because of space restrictions in tube and other small bore tunnels, much of the laying of tracks in these tunnels is still carried out piece-small, using manual methods but using power tools and aids wherever possible. This has the added complication in tube tunnels that night possessions for renewal work are short and track has to be made safe each morning for a further day's running.

Fig. 5.10. Modern main line track installation.

5.27 Day-to-day maintenance of track

The passage of trains coupled with the effects of varied weather and day/night conditions, causes steady deterioration of even the best constructed railway track unless proper day-to-day maintenance is carried out.

Activities of others alongside the railway and trespassers and vandals on the railway can also effect track conditions of safety.

Both visual inspection of condition and mechanical measurement of track geometry is necessary to establish a quality standard and to determine whether the standard is being maintained or not.

Fig. 5.11. Day time maintenance gang at work.

All railways require a track maintenance organisation to ensure adequate inspection is carried out and that proper resources are available to attend to minor matters on the track and immediate surroundings as they arise.

On surface lines, where it is possible to safely stand to one side to allow trains to pass, much daily inspection and local adjustment can be carried out during traffic hours.

On underground railways or other urban railways where clearances are tight and trains are frequent, access for staff is not usually available during traffic hours. In this case maintenance staff must be organised to be on duty at night during non-traffic hours. For these railways all inspection and adjustment of track must be done at night and cannot be watched or further adjusted during the following day except under special protection arrangements which will inevitably delay trains.

Regular major maintenance activities which will obstruct traffic or endanger staff, need to be arranged during non-traffic hours or in a 'possession' of the track specifically arranged for the purpose. Such major activities might well include ballast tamping, drain rodding, rubbish clearing, block joint changing, fence repairs close to the track and replacing individual damaged sleepers, chair castings or rails.

Further Reading

More detailed information on track may be found in 'British Railway Track', Sixth Edition 1993, published by The Permanent Way Institution.

CHAPTER 6

Earthworks, Drainage and Fencing

6.1 Stability of earthworks

Most surface railways involve substantial amounts of earthwork to produce a near as possible level or gently sloping surface upon which to construct the track.

Traditionally in the design of a new railway, a route and mean level were chosen as far as possible to balance cut and fill. This avoided the need for 'borrow' pits and spoil heaps, at the expense of transporting the excavated material from one cut to another area of filling.

Although this approach is quite sound when considering first cost, it can lead to the use of unsatisfactory materials, unstable slopes and the building-in of long term maintenance problems which are difficult and costly to solve. It is vital therefore at the design stage to consider carefully the availability of suitable material for embankments, how these materials should be placed and compacted and at what angle of natural repose the slopes can be expected to be stable in the long term. Proper soil mechanics investigation of the materials excavated in cuttings will determine whether or not they are suitable for transporting to other sites for fill. Railway embankments require much greater strength than highway embankments since the loading intensity is greater at formation level.

Similarly, cutting slopes must vary in steepness in relation to the natural ground conditions through which the cutting passes. Soil mechanics tests can establish the natural angle of repose of each stratum and the slope must be designed accordingly. These slopes will vary in practice from near vertical in hard rock to flatter than 1 in 3 for the softer clays .

Ground water is a vital factor in slope stability. Both in cuttings and embankments, surface water must be channelled to storm water drains or natural water courses. Where drains are either non-existent or blocked, progressive softening of the earthwork structure will take place probably resulting in slipping.

6.2 Short term considerations

When earthworks are composed mainly of cohesive materials, stability will be ensured in the short to medium term only if a state of equilibrium exists at potential cylindrical slip surfaces. This equilibrium exists when the mass of the material contained above the surface, tending to slide downwards and outwards i.e. to rotate, is adequately resisted by the shear strength of the material.

Design of earthworks should be left to specialists in this area and is outside the scope of this textbook. However, all railway engineers should be aware of the basic mechanics of slope stability and be on the look-out for any signs of moving, particularly in areas where clays, mudstones and shales are present. As well as full failure of slopes, local minor slipping due to erosion can cause track level and line irregularities and needs to be watched and remedied before serious movement develops.

6.3 Long Term Considerations

Over-consolidated clays and similar soils can deteriorate in the very long term and earthworks containing such materials can fail after many decades of satisfactory service. As has already been mentioned, ground water and the position of the water table can also have a significant effect. When checking stability of slopes in these areas, strength parameters derived from many old failed sites should be used rather than those derived from locally obtained soil samples.

Fig. 6.1. A well maintained embankment slope.

6.4 Slips

Any movement of the surface layers of a slope as a body can be classified as a slip. When this occurs, the profile of the slope is changed, usually becoming steeper towards the top and with an upwards 'heaving' of the slope towards the toe of the slope.

Slips in both embankments and cutting slopes can occur for a number of reasons. It is essential that the causes of a slip are fully investigated and clearly established before major remedial measures are adopted. Immediate measures, like subjecting traffic to speed restriction and/or providing additional temporary support to track, may well be necessary but careful watching of any development is essential in the early stages of any movement.

Local geology needs to be checked, particularly to see if there are any significant variations in shear strength or permeability of materials. Also water level variations and drains need to be checked. Progressive weathering or repeated wetting and drying or freezing may also cause problems in certain stratum.

Other factors that might be associated with slips or be a cause of 'triggering' include the following:

- Deep cracks which form in some clays in prolonged dry weather.
- Trenches or cultivation close to the tops of cutting slopes or the toes of embankments.
- Heavy materials tipped near the tops of embankments e.g. track ballast, or surcharge from plant/materials near the tops of cutting slopes.
- Long term ash tipping on embankments causing water pockets to collect in the body of the earthwork, progressively softening the clay beneath.

6.5 Detection of movement of earthworks

It is rare for large scale movement of earthworks to occur without there being warning signs beforehand. It cannot be too strongly emphasised that in this area, prevention is far better than cure and the object should always be to identify and cure any problems before they develop into emergencies.

Local track staff and others employed about the railway should be encouraged to look out for and report immediately any of the following:

- Distorted, leaning or dipping signal posts, cable runs or fence lines.
- Tree trunks tipping significantly away from the vertical.
- Cess heave or loss of cess.
- Large cracks in ground surface at any location.
- Local loss of line and level of track which recurs after correction.

Once any of the above 'tell-tale' signs are reported, the local engineer should visit the site without delay and endeavour to establish by simple observation of the site as a whole whether or not serious movement is occurring or could soon occur.

At that stage, unless immediate action is obviously necessary, it would be wise to drive lines of stakes over the slope area concerned to further establish the degree and direction of movement. If it is suspected that a slip circle failure is developing, a grid of plastic tubes can be placed into the ground over the area concerned in holes prebored by driven-in steel pipes. After a short period of time, the level of the slip surface can be 'plumbed' by insertion of a steel mandril placed into the plastic tubes. With these simple techniques, the engineer can establish the extent of the potential slip, both on the surface and in depth.

6.6 Dealing with embankment slips

When an embankment slip is accompanied by loss of material from the cess of the track formation, the top width of the embankment must be immediately made good before traffic can be allowed to recommence. The placing of this fill could well restart movement of the slip unless proper stabilisation measures are taken further down the embankment slope. Although the immediate filling of the lost cess should be in material that is not too heavy, for obvious reasons, care must be taken, if it is porous, not to build-in future problems caused by softening of clay below. Any free draining material placed in this location therefore must be either provided with a drainage pipe system to channel water to and away from the bottom of the embankment, or should be grouted once in position to assist stability and improve surface run-off.

In general terms, embankment slips can be stabilised by one or other of the following methods, or a combination of them:

- Sheet or bored piling
- Berming and/or gabions
- Grouting
- Redraining with counterforts and/or 'herring-bone' drains

The selection of the method to be adopted for stabilisation of any particular embankment will depend on local circumstances, availability of acceptable filling materials, access for plant and the root cause of the slip.

Piling, whether steel sheet or concrete bored, is carried out in the region of the bottom third of the embankment slope and must be deep enough to stitch the embankment together, across the shear plane of the slip circle.

Berming consists of constructing a small embankment in heavy free draining material against the slipped foot of the main embankment, to act as a counterweight. To be effective, the berm must be placed within the slip circle and as near as possible to its lower extremity. Care must be taken in siting the berm to ensure that it does not block any existing drains or overlie any cable runs or other fixed equipment. Before construction of the berm, vegetation should be stripped from the existing embankment surface to avoid any possible future sliding of the berm on the slippery surface produced by decayed vegetation.

The gabion is a useful device to use in the construction of berms or retaining walls. Gabions consist of wire mesh cages into which is placed heavy broken material such as uniform broken stone or broken out mass concrete. The value of this is that the material is confined and can be placed in an interlocking position and is able to stand at a steeper angle than unconfined tipped material. Gabions are most useful where a substantial stabilising weight is required where space is limited. They can also be stacked one upon the other. By the time the wire cages fail through corrosion, vegetation, soil and roots will have grown into the gabions ensuring overall long term stability.

Grouting of embankments is a highly specialist operation requiring 'know-how' and specialist equipment. For this reason, railway engineers who consider this type of ground treatment would be well advised to seek specialist advice, both in investigation and in carrying out any grouting work. It must also be remembered that it is very possible in the early stages of grouting to make the situation worse due to the lubricating effect that grout might have on the slip plane.

This said, grouting can be very effective if properly carried out in suitable locations. The author knows of a number of sites where embankment grouting has been carried out successfully and where embankments with poor history of movement have remained trouble free after grouting for over twenty five years.

Where penetration of surface water into the structure of the embankment is the main problem, attention to drainage often is the best solution. 'Counterforts' should be constructed on the embankment sides at right angles to the tracks. These are trenches with sloping bottoms containing a series of steps and open jointed pipes collecting water and conveying it direct to the bottom of the embankment. The trenches are backfilled with hardcore, broken stone or other large well draining material. Herring-bone pattern

Fig. 6.2. Counterforts and Herring-bone Drainage.

side drains are also often placed between the counterforts to intercept surface water and channel it to the counterfort main drains. At the bottom of the counterforts, the drains are connected to a toe drain which conveys the water away to a water course, soak-away or storm water drain.

6.7 Dealing with cutting slips

When dealing with slips in cuttings, the engineer needs to remember that in this case, unlike in embankment slips, the material that has slipped is likely to have been in its original position from before the construction of the railway. The cause of the slip will therefore be external to the material.

It is again essential to investigate any cutting movement before major works are put in hand and to understand the reasons for the slipping.

The root cause of a cutting slip is likely to be one of the following:

- Erosion of the cutting face due to weathering.

- Building activities or excavation near to the top of the cutting.
- Drainage blockages, modifications or sudden increase in flow.
- Tree roots blocking drains or overhanging trees levering cutting surfaces.
- Progressive softening of slopes caused by trapped ground water or water running through porous layers and running down cutting slopes to cohesive strata below.

It is often the case that slipping of a cutting will cause upwards heaving of the nearest track which might well be very dangerous for traffic.

If there is room in the cess, short term relief may be obtained by sheet piling or weighting down the bottom of the slip by gabions, but care must be taken not to damage or block drainage. Again, as in the case of embankments, there are a number of techniques that can be used to assist restoration of stability and these are all listed under the section on embankments.

Rock cuttings may present particular problems which may need other treatment. In these cases the sides of the cuttings are often almost perpendicular and trains may be endangered by relatively small pieces of weathered rock falling from above. If this occurs, specialist advice should be sought. Possible solutions include rock bolting, wire meshing, guniting and in very bad cases, construction of rock shelters.

6.8 Drainage of the trackbed

Usually the trackbed is laid on natural ground that has had the topsoil removed (the sub-grade). If this is the case, the control of water in the trackbed is a major factor in designing the construction layers in relation to the sub-grade material. Materials that are commonly encountered in sub-grades are as follows:

- Non-cohesive materials like gravel and sand.
- Cohesive Clays and slits.
- Organic peats and silts etc.
- Sedimentary rocks like sandstone or limestone.
- Igneous rocks like granite.

- Metamorphic rocks like slate.

Non-cohesive soils drain well and normally make good sub-grades.

Cohesive soils generally have extremely small pores between their particles and therefore have very low permeability. In this case rainwater falling on the track needs to be collected in the ballast and channelled to drains before it gets to the sub-grade. In the long term, if water is allowed to pond at the cohesive sub-grade, progressive softening will occur and track settlement will begin to show itself.

Peat is a particularly difficult sub-grade to build on and should be investigated by specialists. It has a variety of textures, will usually shrink if drained or if subjected to repeated loading. The behaviour of this material also varies considerably depending on the degree of compaction or overburden it has been subjected to. Wrong treatment of track drainage in areas of peat sub-grade can result in large long term settlements not only of the track but also of adjacent buildings, embankments and fixed installations.

Sedimentary and metamorphic rocks are often permeable by water and often contain springs and lenses or layers of other materials. They are usually much stronger in the unweathered state than cohesive soils and provided that there are suitable means of drainage, will provide a satisfactory sub-grade, even if waterlogged.

Igneous rocks like granite or basalt are hard and impermeable and are unlikely to give any problems as sub-grade for track.

6.9 Sand blankets

A sand blanket is a permeable layer of fine granular material which is placed immediately over a cohesive sub-grade to act as a drainage layer. To prevent water reaching the cohesive sub-grade, it is recommended to place a layer of plastic sheeting on the sub-grade before placing the sand blanket. The blanket should be more than 100 mm thick with a geotextile layer above it under the track ballast.

The term 'geotextile' means a permeable woven fabric-like material made from polymerised resins as used in civil engineering road and other construction. In this application, the geotextile layer is designed to act as a separator to prevent ballast particles entering the blanket. The sand used for blankets should be nominal '3 mm down sharp' or 'angular' with at least 80% passing the 2.36 mm BS Test Sieve and not more than 4% passing the 0.075 mm sieve. The sand should not contain any very fine silt or exhibit plasticity.

6.10 Side or 'Cess' drains

The top surface of the sub-grade should be dressed off to a slope of not flatter than 1 in 25 from the centre down to the cesses so that percolated surface water will flow to the cess drains.

Drainage systems which collect surface water from the ballast should be placed at a minimum depth consistent with avoiding ponding of water in the ballast or in the sand blanket. Tests have generally indicated that about 80% of rainwater reaches side drains direct via track ballast, the remainder penetrating to lower levels and/or the sand blanket and almost all of the rain will reach the drains within an hour of falling.

Cess drains run parallel to tracks and are usually either open jointed glazed earthenware, galvanised corrugated steel or perforated PVC or polypropylene. The side drains should be surrounded in ballast or other free draining material. They must be laid to a sufficient fall to ensure free flowing and provided with catchpits at intervals not longer than 30 m, required for rodding purposes. The catchpits should have removable top grills to allow removal of silt and their sumps must be at least 450 mm below the level of the lowest drain.

6.11 Centre drains

Where there are more than one pair of tracks, it may be necessary to have a drainage run in the 'eight-foot' between the two pairs of tracks or even in the 'six-foot' on a single pair of tracks where very wet conditions can occur.

In this case, the drains will be similar to cess drains and will also require similar catchpits. It may be necessary to relocate some sleepers or even cut some short to accommodate these catchpits. Centre drains should be piped to cess drains wherever convenient.

6.12 Drain cleaning

All drainage pipes must be regularly inspected and rodded when necessary. This consists of pushing rods through pipes with a 'badger' or wood block on the end which is a loose fit to the bore. The rods are flexible with screw threaded ends and further sections are added as blockages are pushed to the next catchpit or manhole. Water jetting or winch-operated cleaning tools can also be used where rodding is not successful.

Catchpits must be cleared out regularly to avoid pipe outlets becoming silted up.

It is always wise to inspect all drainage soon after heavy rain, or if possible during a heavy downpour as it is then that any problems will be best observed.

Fig. 6.3. Pump train for catchpit clearing.

Permanent way drains often discharge into streams, ponds or other watercourses outside the railway boundary. It is wise in these circumstances to inspect these points of discharge to ensure that they have not become blocked.

Where railway drains discharge into storm water drains, arrangements must be made with the appropriate water authority to periodically inspect the out fall and to ensure that any 'back-flaps' or other devices are properly working to ensure that no backflow can occur onto the railway in flood conditions.

6.13 Ineffective drains

However well laid, drains cannot perform their full function if water is not able to reach them. A drain may, on inspection, be apparently in good condition but not taking water from the ballast. If this is the case a full investigation of the ballast content and condition must be carried out as it is likely that it has become clogged, silted or clayed-up over a long period of time. If the ballast has become impermeable in this way, it is usually necessary to replace the ballast as soon as possible. Where drains are deep, it may be helpful to supplement by the addition of shallow collector drains.

In clay soil, the porous filling around drains may also need to be replaced and the collars of open jointed pipes may need to be opened out and cleared periodically.

Occasionally pipes break and cause blockages. This will usually be discovered when rodding is difficult or impossible at a given location. This situation must not be left or it will progressively deteriorate over a period, possibly causing extensive damage to the track structure. When blocking cannot be cleared by rodding, there is no simple alternative but to investigate further by opening up from the surface.

6.14 Railway fencing

In most developed countries, railways need to be fenced off, both to define ownership boundaries and to keep animals, children and would-be trespassers away from the tracks.

Fig. 6.4. Drainage catchpits.

Fig. 6.5. Fence for third/fourth rail electrified railway.

In the UK, all railways must be fenced with a sturdy barrier to a minimum height of 1350 mm. On railways which have third and/or fourth rail electrification, the fences must be of the 'unclimbable' type such as chain link, weldmesh or wire mesh. Care needs to be taken at footbridges and other locations where handrails and footholds occur that the unclimbable fence is taken up a clear 1350 mm above such levels.

Arrangements must be made for regular inspection of all fences and urgent attention given to any defects that are reported. In addition to periodic fence inspections, all staff who walk or patrol the track must be specifically instructed to look out for and immediately report any defects seen during other duties and any cases of trespass or straying by animals.

It is only with such vigilance on the part of all staff on or about the railway, that serious incidents and accidents can be avoided.

All structures over and under railways must be provided with adequate parapets as defined and stipulated by various authorities. It is essential that fences adequately link with these parapets in such a way as not to leave any gaps or foot holds for access onto the railway. Any authorised gates through the boundary fence for use of railway staff must be properly locked.

CHAPTER 7

Bridges and Structures

7.1 Early railway structures and materials

The building of railways always involves the construction of structures, both to support the railway and its infrastructure, and to carry buildings, roads and other forms of transport over or alongside the railway. As well as this, many stations and ancillary buildings involve complex structures, sometimes spanning large distances or covering a considerable area, as in the case of a large terminal station.

Early railway engineers used materials and structural forms which had been well tried in other industrial buildings and transport systems. This included, in particular, brickwork, masonry, timber, cast and wrought iron, generally in the form of massive gravity walls, arches, simple beams and latticed or trussed structures.

Although heavy timber work was used for early load bearing structures, notably trestle viaducts, this deteriorated quickly and was largely replaced by more permanent materials by the end of the nineteenth century.

Cast iron proved to be a good material to use in conditions of direct compression but was found to be unreliable in flexural bending in the tension zones. After a number of accidents which caused bridge collapses in early days, cast iron was banned from new bridges in areas of tensile stress. Rivetted wrought iron however performed well over a long period of repeated loading and was very satisfactory in both compression and tension.

Fig. 7.1. Laminated timber arched bridge at Lancaster.

This material was used for all bridge members subject to bending up to the end of the nineteenth century when steel making was perfected.

Where there was sufficient construction depth available, the well tried arch form was used for many bridges both over and under the tracks. Provided that the materials are sound and the structure is well maintained, the expected life of an arch structure is almost indefinite, even when subjected to dynamic live load.

Cast iron arches have satisfactorily carried railway loading for periods in excess of a hundred years. In this case the stresses are mainly direct compression, although some tension can occur on skew bridges which require regular examination. Where tension stresses do occur in cast iron arches under dynamic rail loading, which can only be ascertained by strain gauge readings, urgent action is required. The cast iron has to be relieved of live load, either by provision of steel undergirdering or possibly by complete encasement in reinforced concrete. In extreme cases, such as at Kilburn illustrated below, complete reconstruction is necessary.

Fig. 7.2. Hundred-year old cast iron arches at Kilburn.

Many wrought iron structures were very intricate with complicated rivetted connections. These connections were often very inaccessible and could not be properly inspected or painted resulting in pockets of corrosion. Bearings to large wrought iron structures often similarly could not be properly maintained and sometimes became virtually fixed. This induced undesirable stresses in the structures in extremes of temperature and put extra forces on supporting substructures.

7.2 Modern welded steelwork

Since the beginning of the twentieth century, structural steel work has been used for the vast majority of metal bridges, both over and under the tracks. Originally hot rivetting techniques, established on wrought ironwork, were adapted and refined for steelwork. Until the early 1940's, all steelwork was shop fabricated using rivetting and joined on site using a mixture of site rivetting and bolting either with 'black' or turned and fitted bolts.

During the Second World War, welding techniques began to be used and by the early 1950's metal arc welding became the standard method of fabricating structures in the works. Site jointing by then had also improved with the introduction of high strength friction grip bolts which were tensioned by a measured torque. Site welding was also used on occasions but only under very strictly controlled conditions.

Modern welded bridge design also aims at keeping all details as clean and simple as possible. This is not only for aesthetic reasons but also to ensure that maintenance and inspection are made as easy as possible and that rain water runs off without collecting in corrosion pockets.

For medium spans, steel bridges are usually constructed with single webbed 'I' section main girders either under the track or alongside with cross girders between to transfer track loads back to the main girders. Care needs to be taken in the design of the connection between the cross girders and the main girders to ensure that the joints are well protected against corrosion.

For longer spans, welded steel bridges are often constructed with main girders in the form of a box. Again, these can be placed either immediately under the track or alongside in a 'through' formation. The advantages with

Fig. 7.3. Reconstructed girder bridge at Kilburn.

box construction are that it is torsionally much stiffer than an 'I' section, can have very clean lines and can have access hatches to inspect the inside of the box which is protected from corrosion.

For double track railway bridges with much larger spans, in excess of about 30 m, the main girders can be in the form of a lattice or truss. Again, with welded construction attention to detail in the design can result in a very clean design which is far easier to maintain than with older rivetted trusses.

Painting methods and preparation need to be very carefully considered on all new steel structures.

On all types of modern welded steel bridges it is essential to ensure that there is good access for inspection and maintenance of main bearings. All bearings should be on concrete plinths to ensure that jacks can be placed alongside to relieve the loads to allow replacement of bearings if necessary during the life of the structure.

Fig. 7.4. Welded truss railway bridge.

Fig. 7.5. Welded tubular station roof at Waterloo.

Station roofs can be constructed in welded steel. For long spans, one of the best forms is welded tubular steel. Again, much care needs to be taken at the design stage to ensure that joints are simple, clean, inspectable and without pockets to collect water. Thought should also be given on large roofs to the proposed method of cleaning of gutters, downpipes and any glazing, and method of inspection and painting.

7.3 Reinforced concrete structures

Mass concrete structures and foundations were in use well before the construction of the first railways. Even the Romans were well versed in the use of cements to bind together natural and manufactured materials and used mortars and mass concrete in many 'gravity' structures.

In such structures, loads were assumed to spread at an angle of about 45°, thus avoiding tensile stresses within the concrete mass. Even in the late

Fig. 7.6. Reinforced concrete station portal frame built in the 1930's.

eighteenth century it was known that concrete was about ten times stronger in compression than in tension.

About the middle of the nineteenth century, a number of systems of reinforced concrete were introduced in France, notably by Monier and Hennebique. By the early twentieth century, reinforced concrete was being used in the UK for railway structures to an increasing degree.

In essence, reinforced concrete combines the compressive strength of concrete with the tensile resistance of mild steel reinforcement. Structures are subject to stress analysis under all combinations of likely loading and the steel reinforcement is introduced where tension will be produced by bending moments, torsion or shear forces or a combination of these.

The main advantage claimed for concrete over steel is that there is no corrosion and the structure does not require painting or maintenance. Although there is some truth in this, it is not the full story. Minute cracks do occur in concrete. These may be caused by shrinkage at the time of casting but proper safeguards during concreting and in the immediately following curing period can reduce these to an acceptable minimum.

Flexure of the structure under load may also produce some cracking of the cover concrete to allow the steel to pick up the tensile strain. Here again following certain design requirements laid down in BS Codes of Practice should reduce such cracking to an acceptable minimum. In exposed locations however, over a number of seasons and climatic variations, it is likely that some moisture will penetrate the surface of reinforced concrete structures. This must be carefully watched as corrosion of reinforcement under apparently sound concrete cover can seriously damage structural integrity. Structures subjected to dynamic loading and/or reversal of bending moments (as on continuous beams) need to be particularly carefully inspected on a regular basis.

Reinforced concrete is particularly useful for structures carrying mainly dead or static loads, such as columns, retaining walls, pile caps, spread foundations, rafts and piers where the dead weight of the concrete in the member under consideration is not too significant.

Where reinforced concrete has been used for long span structures carrying only a relatively small amount of superimposed load e.g. snow and wind, the extra dead load produced by the reinforced concrete structure coupled with the need to control and counteract cracking has often made it uneconomical in the long term. Long span station roofs and footbridges in reinforced concrete can often come into this category. This is the case even after allowing for savings arising from the fact that no periodic painting is required.

Simple components which are not subjected to excessive loads or moments are often very satisfactorily constructed in precast reinforced concrete. These include components for platforms, staircases, subways, cable ducts and runs, walkways, fence posts, sand bins, catchpits and small lineside cabins.

On modern railway bridge superstructure construction, reinforced concrete is often used in conjunction with welded steelwork or prestressed concrete as part of the bridge deck and often forms the parapets.

Reinforced concrete is usually used today in the substructure, abutments and wing walls in place of mass concrete, brickwork or masonry, purely because it is more economical in both materials and excavation costs.

Early reinforced concrete was compacted manually and often was laid with too wet a mix resulting in poor density. Today careful control of the water/cement ratio and compaction by mechanical vibrators ensures a stronger and more dense and durable material.

7.4 Prestressed concrete

Concrete is about ten times as strong in compression as it is in tension. Reinforced concrete simply overcomes this deficiency by adding steel reinforcement where tension is likely to occur. Although this is completely satisfactory, it does lead to heavy structures as up to half of the concrete is not contributing to the structural strength. This is particularly so on long span structures or where reversal of bending is likely under dynamic loading.

This disadvantage is largely overcome by the introduction of prestressing. Simply put, this is a technique of introducing a pre-compression into the concrete in areas where tension would otherwise develop under loading, which is at least equal to the applied tension, thus negating that tensile stress. In this way, the whole concrete section remains under compression and therefore 'works'.

Fig. 7.7. Railway bridge reconstructed using pretensioned prestressed concrete beams.

In general terms, there are two methods of introducing prestress to a concrete member. The first is known as 'pretensioning'. This involves applying tension to wires which are set into a mould and then concreted in. These wires or strands are fully bonded to the surrounding concrete and once the concrete has hardened and acquired sufficient strength the wires are cut thus applying a compressive force to the surrounding concrete. This method is usually applied under factory conditions and is largely used for small repetitative units like beams, sleepers, planks, ducts and lintels etc. It is also often known as the 'long line' method of prestressing.

The second method of prestressing is more often used for larger units and is known as 'post-tensioning'. As the name implies, in this method the tensioning is carried out after the casting of the concrete. Units are provided with cast-in ducts and anchorages and the prestressing tendons are stressed up once the concrete has achieved sufficient strength and then held in tension by some form of wedging at the anchorages.

With larger beams, it is quite common for segmental units to be cast in a transportable size and stressed together on site. After tensioning of the prestressing tendons, the ducts are usually fully grouted up under pressure with cement grount. The joints between the precast segments are usually filled with an epoxy mortar or can be left dry if they have been carefully cast against one another in the works thus ensuring accurate fit.

Fig. 7.8. Concrete segmental box girder units.

Epoxy mortar can be used in a variety of ways with concrete and other structural materials where early strength is required. One disadvantage, however that must be watched, particularly when working at night or during possessions, is that certain materials will not 'go off' at low temperatures. Prior advice should be sought from manufacturers on the lowest air temperature that will allow the proposed materials to set before using in possession.

7.5 Bridge reconstruction

For new railways, methods of construction of bridges and other structures are very similar to those adopted for any other civil engineering project.

On existing railways however, the design and construction methods that have to be adopted are largely dictated by the absolute requirement to continue to operate trains safely during the construction period.

Superstructures for bridges and structures, both over and under railway tracks, need to be constructed during possession of the railway, at night or week-ends when railway traffic is at its lightest

Often, it is possible to carry out work on substructures during railway traffic hours but this often involves prior construction of temporary or protective works during possession of the tracks. The conventional method of reconstruction of abutments is to install 'waybeams' under possession to carry tracks in the immediate area of the new abutment. These waybeams can be supported on timber cribs or pads or piles. This then allows construction of the new abutment beneath, although it is usual to impose a speed restriction on trains crossing the temporary works.

Various other methods of construction of substructures have been adopted, avoiding the use of waybeams. These mainly relate to various methods of jacking precast units into position laterally from jacking pits on either side of the track. Smaller units can be thrust into position using similar pipe-jacking or thrust-boring techniques. It is also possible to construct deep pile foundations on either side of the track and incorporate cill beams in the superstructure that will carry the loads onto the side piles.

Where large span railway bridges have foundations in tidal waters, thorough investigation must be made into the condition of foundations and the various alternative methods that are open for reconstruction and/or strengthening.

Superstructures for railway bridges on existing lines can be placed in position by one of the following basic methods:

- Piece-small lifting in
- Complete lifting in
- Lateral rolling-in or sliding-in
- Wrap-round

Fig. 7.9. Erection of New Girders, Lune Viaduct.

- Launching
- Tailor made method e.g. Lune Viaduct

Lateral repositioning of bridge superstructures has for many decades been done using steel balls running in the web of bullhead rail. The rolling-in trolley usually incorporates a one hundred ton capacity jack and the lateral pull to move the bridge is provided by cable winches, either manual or power driven. In recent years, heavy bridges have been slid into position rather than rolled using skates surfaced with PTFE. This is a very slow operation but can be carefully controlled and bridges weighing well over a thousand ton have been moved into position using this method with a possible positional accuracy within 15 mm.

In this method, large bridges are usually moved into position about 100 mm higher than their final level and then jacked down once in the correct location on plan.

Rail mounted rail cranes are available for lifts of units on most main line railways. These are usually limited in capacity to not more than 75 tons at

Fig. 7.10. 100 ton Rolling-in trolley.

minimum radius and may be required at short notice to deal with derailments or other emergencies.

Where it is possible to get road mounted cranes to the site of the work, these are often of more use due to their flexibility in operation and increased capacity and reach. It is now possible to hire road cranes with a capacity of up to 500 tons, or even more.

Special precautions need to be taken when using both road and rail cranes on railways having overhead electrification.

7.6 Brick and masonry structures

Many early bridges over and under railways were constructed in brick or masonry, usually adopting some form of arched construction. The methods had been well tried over the preceding centuries on the building of roads, canals and aqueducts. Today, there are still examples of such structures built almost two thousand years ago by the Romans, that demonstrate the basic stability of masonry arches.

Railway bridges constructed both over and under tracks incorporating arches usually last as long as the railway and will only be demolished if widening of the span is necessary or higher headroom is required for overhead electrification.

The experience gained in carrying out such arch demolitions on British Rail prior to electrification, showed the high intrinsic strength of most arches. The only occasional exception to this is on skew arches or those which are very flat, as one might expect.

A prerequisite for long term stability of an arch is unyielding supports and foundations. Many perfectly sound arches have collapsed due to movement of other parts of the main structure, foundations or supporting ground. It is imperative therefore that much care is given to both design and maintenance of all supports when adopting any form of arched construction.

Masonry and brick gravity walls, abutments and piers similarly can continue for very long periods without much attention. It is important to keep joints well pointed and any drainage well rodded to ensure that water

Fig. 7.11. Brick Arched Underbridge still giving good service after 150 years.

does not get into the structure. Such percolation of water can cause deterioration, particularly due to frost action and washing out of 'fines'.

In very large masonry piers it is wise to check internal condition by trial bores at different levels. Any voids that are found or softness of material should be pressure grouted to prevent further deterioration.

Because of high labour costs, it is not usual today to use masonry or brickwork for large gravity structures. If appearance is a consideration, structures can be constructed in concrete and then faced in brick or masonry.

7.7 Examination of structures

All bridges, structures and buildings which form part of the railway infrastructure need to be carefully inspected at regular intervals by suitably qualified and experienced staff. Most railway authorities inspect in detail all bridges and other structures which are subjected to dynamic loading at least every four years, as well as carrying out superficial inspections on an annual basis. Any matter that comes to light in either the annual or detailed inspection may mean that the structure is subjected to special inspection at more frequent intervals.

The aim of the annual superficial examination is to bring to notice any significant deterioration in condition, any development of new cracks or worsening of old cracks, any sign of impact from vehicles or serious vandalism, walls out of plumb or similar developments which might place the railway at risk. Whenever possible the structure should be observed under traffic to note any undue vibration, deflection, looseness or separation of parts and to observe its general behaviour.

In addition to the inspections carried out by specialist examiners, permanent way patrolmen and others walking about the railway should be instructed to report any defect or change to condition that is noticed on structures.

Each railway authority must devise its own method of numbering all structures and recording inspections and work carried out thereon. Records must be kept up to date and always available to responsible people who 'need to know'. Where possible, such records should be kept on computer with back-up records kept at separate locations in case of loss by fire, theft or vandalism etc. The unique number that is given to each bridge or structure should be displayed on at least two number plates fixed permanently to the structure.

Some railway authorities number each line with a pre-fix letter e.g. MR 90 (bridge number 90 on the former Metropolitan Railway) or by referring to the location from the main terminus e.g. 96M 20 ch (bridge 96 miles 20 chains from Paddington) or give the line and then the number e.g. London–Birmingham No 59. Care needs to be taken, especially at intersections of railway lines that all structures are given a unique number and that there is no duplication. This is particularly important where new bridges are built over existing lines or where old structures are modified or removed. When a new structure is completed, it is important that 'as-built' drawings are provided to the inspection office and that contract or design drawings are not assumed to be as actually constructed on site. This should be the prime responsibility of the resident engineer on any project before matters are finally wound up on site.

7.8 Structural maintenance

As in many other areas of railway engineering, proper maintenance of structures is essential if they are to be kept in satisfactory service for a maximum period.

As mentioned previously, regular inspection of all structures must be programmed and from this, maintenance schedules should be drawn up.

Certain maintenance works such as painting of steelwork, gutter cleaning and drain rodding should be carried out on a regular cycle basis. Other work will largely rise from inspection and will be on an 'as-and-when' basis. This would include such items as brickwork repairs and repointing, bearing replacement and minor steelwork repairs.

Structural maintenance work can be dramatically reduced in cost by attention to detail at the design and construction stage. Good examples of this are ensuring that bearings can be properly inspected and replaced without costly temporary works to support the bridge and the reduction of corrosion pockets to a minimum. Similarly, good inspection procedures should ensure that potential weaknesses are spotted and dealt with at an early stage before too much damage takes place.

7.9 Strength assessment

Running in parallel with proper maintenance and inspection procedures, all railways need to have a specialist team engaged upon assessment of strength of all existing structures. This involves what may be described as a 'designing backwards' exercise.

Bridge Assessment is made necessary by the general increase of loads being carried by highways, the variation of loading on railways as speeds increase and axle spacings widen and the general deterioration of some structural materials through age.

Based upon the condition survey which arises out of the four yearly detailed inspection, engineers can calculate the likely stresses that will occur under maximum loading at critical points. Site measurement of remaining metal coupled with testing to destruction of samples taken from non-critical locations on the structure or certain non-destructive tests will then allow accurate analysis of the actual residual strength of the structure.

Any resulting calculated overstress will then be carefully considered to see if any relief can be obtained to critical members by local strengthening or propping or by imposing speed restrictions. If none of these measures are acceptable or effective in the longer term, then consideration must be given to reconstruction.

This chapter has only given a very broad outline of the whole subject of railway bridges and structures. Students that wish to read further are recommended to enquire in the Library of the Institution of Civil Engineers, Great George Street, London SW1P 3AA and in the following books known to the author:

Frank Turton, *Railway Bridge Maintenance* (Hutchinson Education Ltd.)
F A W Mann, *Railway Bridge Construction* (Hutchinson Education Ltd.)
P S A Berridge, *The Girder Bridge* (Robert Maxwell–Pergamon Press Ltd.)

CHAPTER 8

Tunnels and Tunnelling

8.1 The history of tunnelling

Wherever possible, the original railway constructors, like the earlier canal builders, followed the valleys and avoided the necessity of tunnelling through hills. However, this was not always possible, and in many locations railway tunnels had to be built. Almost always this meant considerable difficulty, delay and expense and frequently loss of life due to the hazards of construction.

On main line railways, tunnelling methods followed those used for the construction of canal tunnels, which in turn had relied heavily on skills learned in the coal, china clay and iron ore mining industries. The work was slow, hard and dangerous, often involving men working in appalling conditions.

Early tunnel construction was carried out by men excavating by hand using pick and shovel, blasting and splitting where necessary in the harder rocks, shoring up with heavy timbers as they progressed slowly forward. On the spot, judgement would be made, depending on the nature of the ground, whether a permanent lining was required or if the tunnel excavation could safely stand unsupported. Many wrong decisions were made on this critical area sometimes with disastrous results and loss of lives. If a lining was deemed necessary, this would usually be in the form of brickwork or stonework which would be constructed behind the miners, the temporary props then being removed as the work progressed.

These early tunnel builders showed considerable skill and courage considering that they were literally working in the dark in relation to the nature of the strata they were likely to encounter and the level and pressure of ground water that could be tapped at any time.

8.2 'Cut-and-cover' tunnels

In built up urban areas, tunnels were sometimes necessary because of space limitations and the requirement to place the tracks below ground level. This was the case in the construction of the first lengths of the Metropolitan and District Lines in London, including now what is called the Circle Line.

Fig. 8.1. Early 'Cut-and-cover' construction in London.

In this case the tunnels were constructed by what has become known as the 'cut-and-cover' method, which is still used today throughout the world for the construction of shallow running tunnels and stations. Its main disadvantage is the considerable disruption it causes at surface level during construction.

8.3 The first tunnel shields

Up to the end of the eighteenth, century no tunnels had been successfully constructed under water courses. Marc Brunel, the father of the more famous Isambard Kingdom Brunel, patented a rectangular 'tunnel shield' in 1818 which he later used on the construction of his Thames Tunnel between Wapping and Rotherhithe. Although the idea was born out of the problem of tunnelling through waterlogged ground, the principle of the moving tunnel shield was then established and is now internationally accepted for all safe tunnelling work in anything other than hard rock.

Marc Brunel's shield was rectangular in shape with individual cells. It consisted of massive cast-iron frames sitting on shoes at the bottom of the excavation, the working face being supported by heavy oak planks or 'poling boards' which were individually held in position by screw jacks bearing on the frames. Each poling board was removed one at a time in each cell, excavated behind by hand to a depth of about 100 mm and then replaced at the new advanced position with the screw jack fully extended. In all, there could be up to thirty six men working at the face at any one time, each in an individual cell. Although safe, this method was painfully slow and encouraged contractors to take short cuts to improve progress.

The story of the construction of the Thames Tunnel is well documented elsewhere, including all the problems that were met. Eventually, these were overcome and the tunnel is still in use today, accommodating the tracks of the East London Line, part of the London Underground. The practicality of use of the tunnel shield was then firmly established by the Brunels, father and son.

Another engineer, Peter Barlow patented a circular shield a little later and one of his students James Greathead developed this further and used it in 1869 to drive a tunnel under the Thames near the Tower of London and later under the Hudson River in New York. The 'Greathead Shield' as it is now known, has basic features which still remain unchanged. These are a protective structure under which the ground can be excavated and an extension in the rear in which the permanent lining of the tunnel can be erected, with jacks which force the shield forward reacting on the completed lining.

The first 'tube' underground railway tunnels built in London using 'Greathead' shields were commenced in 1886 and now form part of the City branch of the London Underground Northern Line.

8.4 Modern tunnel shields

Modern tunnel shields used for soft ground tunnelling follow the same basic principles as the 'Greathead' shield. Some sophistication has been added in the form of hydraulic jacking and 'steering', hydraulic arms at the rear to assist in the positioning of tunnel lining segments and power operated tools of various types to excavate the face as well as improved equipment for probing ahead.

Fig. 8.2. Modern soft ground tunnel shield.

8.5 Differing ground conditions

The method of construction and the design of the final tunnel structure are very much dictated by the nature of the ground through which the tunnel passes. Careful and thorough site investigation of the geology and the water conditions is an essential prerequisite of successful tunnelling. Bore holes are usually sunk close to but not immediately on the line of the proposed tunnel, to probe the strata and to deduce as far as possible the contours of the materials which are likely to be encountered.

In extreme conditions, the line or level of the proposed tunnel may be modified to avoid poor ground conditions discovered in the survey. This preliminary information will also be made available to tenderers to enable an estimate to be made of any special precautions, such as ground stabilization or working in compressed air, which may be needed.

8.6 Construction methods

Tunnels which are 'bored', rather than constructed following excavation down from the surface, need to adopt various building techniques depending on a number of factors. These factors will include the following considerations:

(i) Material through which the tunnel is likely to pass, including the consistency of that material or the likely degree of variation.
(ii) Any faults or pockets likely in the strata including those likely to convey local high water pressure.
(ii) The level of the water table and any water bearing non-cohesive material likely to be met like 'running' sand.
(iv) Any disturbance to the original ground that could have occurred previously and then temporarily stabilized. This situation might occur when driving a second tunnel close to a previous tunnel or adjacent to existing foundations, basements or sewers.
(v) Substantial variation in imposed ground pressures, either vertically or horizontally, caused by heavy buildings above or immediately alongside the line of the proposed tunnel.

(vi) The length of the proposed tunnel and the speed it is required to build it. Tunnel construction speeds are generally slow but if considerable lengths have to be constructed it is often worth spending extra money on more sophisticated equipment to increase building speed.

In all civil engineering construction, safety is an essential ingredient. In tunnelling, this is an absolutely primary consideration and must never be allowed to become secondary to considerations of cost or speed of construction.

Each tunnel construction operation must be carefully considered on its own merits looking at all the factors listed above. A 'Method Statement' should then be agreed between the engineer and the contractor before operations commence and plant is agreed. The Method Statement should clearly define not only the methods of working but the agreed procedure when work stops between shifts or for longer periods at weekends etc. and the monitoring of movement of the ground above as the work proceeds.

Very accurate surveying of tunnel work, both as the operations proceed and after completion, is essential so that any necessary corrections of line or level can be applied as the work progresses. Railway tunnels usually have very tight clearances to rolling stock and any misalignment in build is difficult if not impossible to compensate in revised track geometry. Even relatively small errors of construction sometimes require a length of tunnel to be rebuilt, which clearly is undesirable and must be guarded against.

8.7 Tunnel linings

Except where tunnels pass through sound rock which is expected to be self-supporting, most tunnels are provided with a permanent lining. When tunnelling in relatively soft ground, the lining can be constructed in masonry, brickwork, cast iron, precast concrete or *in situ* concrete.

Bolted cast iron and concrete segments are usually pressure grouted behind to fill any voids.

Certain types of precast reinforced concrete segments are expanded against the clay and provided with wedge or key sections and do not require grouting.

Fig. 8.3. Expanded concrete linings.

The New Austrian Tunnelling Method (NATM) has been used extensively for a number of railway tunnels in Europe and beyond and is now being used in the UK. Some early difficulties were experienced in the UK, notably for the Heathrow Express, and great care is necessary in this method, particularly in the early excavation stages.

The system involves an immediately sprayed concrete shell applied to the excavated bore followed later by a permanent *in situ* shuttered concrete lining.

Most long drives of soft ground tunnelling for running tunnels are constructed using some form of tunnel boring machine (TBM) which are purpose built for each large contract. This machine usually thrusts itself forward by some system of hydraulic jacks bearing on the completed tunnel lining.

Conventional station tunnels may often be built by hand, a pilot tunnel having first been machine built as part of the running tunnel drive.

8.8 Vertical and sloping shafts

All but the very shortest railway tunnels require some vertical shafts, both for the purpose of construction, and for final ventilation or draught relief.

These shafts are build 'top down' each ring being completed and grouted before the next lower is started beneath it. Segments are individually manoeuvred into position by hand, the space required having been carefully excavated rather like in underpinning. As rings are completed, the 'dumpling' inside the shaft can be excavated by machine loading into buckets and craned away or simply 'grabbed' out by crane. Much care must be taken when water or running sand is encountered where special precautions may be necessary.

Sloping shafts are necessary for the use of escalators, usually at about thirty degrees to the horizontal. These are constructed in a similar manner and can be very difficult to build, especially nearer the surface when going through made ground and surface water pockets. Escalator shafts often require

Fig. 8.4. Concrete lined vertical shaft.

dewatering, pressure grouting, chemical grouting, ground freezing or other ground treatment and need careful investigation well before starting operations.

8.9 Tunnel inspection and maintenance

Well constructed tunnels should require little maintenance, especially if they are relatively dry. However, access has to be arranged for tunnels to be inspected in detail on a regular basis. The frequency should be based on the general condition of the tunnel, its material of construction and the amount of water present.

Records must be kept of all inspections and repairs and the amount of ingress of water. Brick tunnels require periodic repointing but most concrete and cast iron lined tunnels require little attention.

Further Reading

Further interesting information on tunnels and tunnelling can be obtained from the library of the Institution of Civil Engineers, referred to at the end of the previous chapter.

There is also interesting historic information on railway tunnelling in the following two books:

H G Follenfant, *Rebuilding London's Underground* (London Transport)
L T C Rolt, *Isambard Kingdom Brunel* (Book Club Associates)

CHAPTER 9

Electrification

9.1 Electricity as a form of motive power

The evolution of various forms of motive power is well covered in Chapter 3 on rolling stock. Reference should be made to that chapter for details. Around the world during the past century there has been debate, sometimes heated and protracted and rarely conclusive, on the best form of motive power for railways. It can be stated however that mainly railways have changed to some form of electric motive power in recent decades and this is the current trend.

This chapter does not therefore address this subject again but looks at the physical, operational and management implications for railways where electrification in some form is adopted.

Electrification is most often applied to railways where the density of traffic movement is sufficient to justify the high fixed costs. Simply put, when there are enough trains, it is more economic to remove the power stations from the engines themselves and instead build bigger but fewer ones at stationary locations.

There is also an apparent conflict between the use of AC and DC. High voltage alternating current (AC) systems tend to have cheaper fixed equipment but more costly locomotives. Medium voltage direct current (DC) systems in contrast have more extensive and costly fixed equipment but cheaper locomotives.

Because electrification systems have developed differently on different systems, there are now several types of locomotive and multiple unit stock that are able to run on both AC and DC current. A notable example of this is the rolling stock running between Paris and London via the Channel Tunnel.

9.2 Generation of electricity

When the first railways were electrified, generation of electricity was also in its infancy. Many railway and tramway companies built their own generating stations to ensure that they were self sufficient. This generation was usually carried out at large steam driven installations which were often sited close to rivers for easy delivery of the large amounts of coal or coke required for firing boilers. In London for instance, the forerunners of the Underground generated electricity at Neasden and Chelsea Creek, and the LCC Tramways had a generating station on the Thames at Greenwich. Because railways often have high demands at peak travel times, these generating stations were not very efficient due to being over capacity for much of the traffic day. The use of electricity in homes became much more widespread between the wars and some railway authorities gradually began to take electricity supply from the National Grid rather than rely completely on their own generating stations. The exception to this was those railways which were mainly underground where loss of power both for traction and lighting could cause very serious life threatening problems.

In most countries now, surface railways rely on the national supply for electrical power.

Underground railways usually make provision for alternative supply sources, sometimes from their own generators, to cover the safety aspects, should the main supply source fail.

9.3 Railway electrification systems

The two most common ways of electrifying main line railways is by the 25 kV AC single phase system at the industrial frequency of 50 Hz or by the

750 V DC system. Metros and light railways also use these systems but lower voltages are often adopted, particularly where some street running is involved. Other electrification systems do exist such as 15 kV AC single phase operating at 16.6 Hz which is found in central Europe, 50 kV in Africa and some DC railways operating with voltages up to 3,000 V. These however are far less common than the two main types described above.

At first sight, the 25 kV AC and the 750 V DC systems appear to be totally different but in fact they do have many common features. This is because, until very recently, electric trains were usually powered by 750 V DC traction motors. The electric power delivered to the trainset must therefore be suitably conditioned so that it can be applied to and used to control the speed and power output of the motor and therefore the speed and performance of the train.

On the DC system, power is taken direct from the National Grid or railway power station at a voltage of 33 kV or 11 kV and is transformed down to a lower voltage at each sub station placed along the route of the railway. These sub stations are usually spaced between 3 and 7 km apart and, after transforming the voltage down to a suitable level, it is rectified and supplied to the conductor rails.

On an AC system railway however, the power is taken from the National Grid at usually 132 kV or even higher. The power is again transmitted down at each feeder station to the normal voltage of 25 kV. These feeder stations need only be spaced about 50 km apart and power is distributed around the network at this voltage by means of an overhead catenary system from which it is collected by the trainset through a sliding contact. The collected power is transformed down to a lower voltage and rectified by equipment on board the train before application to the DC traction motors.

The essential difference then between the AC and DC systems of electrification is that on the DC system, the electric power is transformed and rectified to its DC form at fixed sub stations distributed along the railway whilst for the AC system the power is transformed and converted in a mobile, on board, sub station. For a high capacity, high density, low speed railway with many trains spaced a few minutes apart, the DC system may well prove to be the most economic. However, for high speed, high power InterCity type trains which run less frequently, the AC system is usually found to be most cost effective.

9.4 The AC system connection of supply

Electrical power is provided to AC railways at intervals between 40 and 60 km. This range of spacing generally ensures adequate voltage levels along the full length of the system under both normal and emergency feeding conditions.

Although in principle it is possible to connect railway supply points at any voltage between 33 kV and 400 kV, the need to limit supply system disturbances usually requires connection at 132 kV or a higher voltage level. The availability of suitable connection points and consideration of cost normally favours connection at 132 kV. The traction supply transformers are single-phase and on the primary side are connected between two phases of the supply authority three-phase systems. Phase pairs are chosen to minimise voltage unbalance. Where possible, the three available phase pairs should be in rotation along a route. This ensures that when a transformer is out of service, the units on either side, which are now electrically adjacent, will not be connected to the same pair of phases.

9.5 AC system feeder points

Under normal conditions each feeder station feeds to a mid-point track sectioning cabin in each direction as shown in Fig. 9.1 below, these being about half-way between feeder stations.

Bus-section circuit breakers are provided at the midpoint cabins which also perform an electrical sectioning and parallelling function. Further sectioning and parallelling of the railway overhead system is provided by intermediate track sectioning cabins

All British Rail 25 kV switch gear is under the control of an Electrical Control Operator. He is able, by means of a remote supervisory control and indication system, to operate all the circuit breakers, including the incoming feeder circuit breaker at feeder stations, from an Electrical Control Room

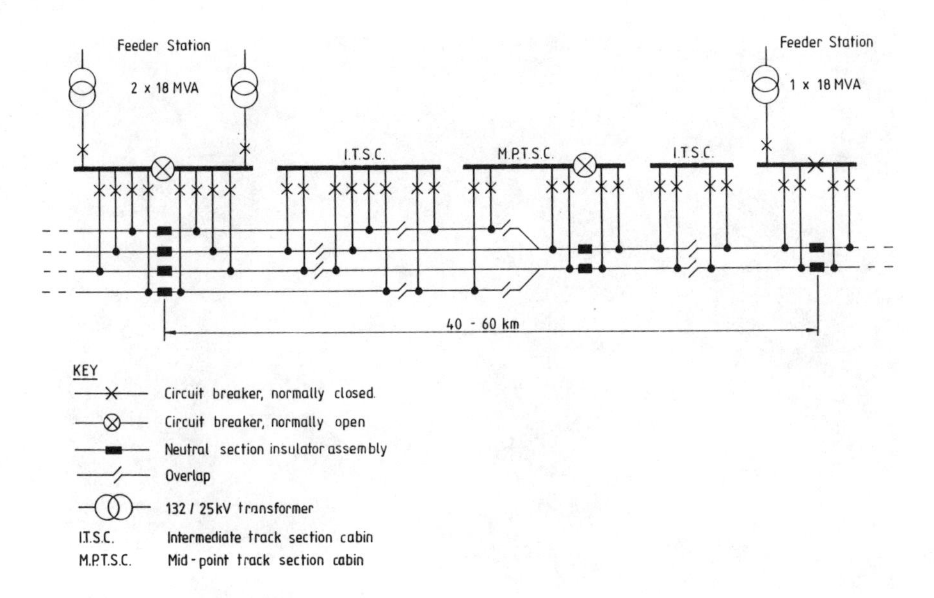

Fig. 9.1. Diagram of typical 25 kV feeding arrangement.

which is manned continuously where the state of the network is displayed on a mimic diagram.

9.6 AC overhead equipment

Power is supplied to the trainset by an overhead catenary system operating at a normal voltage of 25 kV. This consists of a nominally horizontal contact wire made from hard drawn copper, suspended by means of wire 'droppers' from a catenary wire cable. The catenary itself is supported on masts or portal frames spaced along the tracks at a maximum spacing of 73 m apart. To equalise the wear of the pantograph carbons, the copper contact wire zig-zags on plan along the centre of the track, the offset at each support point being 230 mm on straight track.

The height of the contact wire above rail level varies between the limits of 4.14 m and 5.94 m to accommodate minimum clearance under bridges and to satisfy statutory requirements at level crossings. Care must be taken

Fig. 9.2. Modern 25 kV overhead equipment.

at locations of limited clearances that no projection is allowed which might cause arcing.

9.7 Earthing on the AC system

The current leaving the trainset first passes into the running rails of the railway. The running rails are connected to one another and the electrification masts at regular intervals, to create a distributed earth along the railway. This distributed earth enables current to pass from the rails into the greater mass of earth and in this way it maintains the rails close to earth potential. This limits the danger to personnel working on or about the railway.

For the same reason, all metalwork which is exposed to touch and may become accidentally energised is also connected to the rails. Exposed metalwork may become energised due to an insulator flashover or by coming into contact with a broken energised conductor. The earthing system also ensures that, in the event of an electrical fault, the current is of sufficient magnitude to operate the protective relays of the railway and thereby open the appropriate circuit breakers to isolate the faulty section.

9.8 Electrical interference

A single phase AC railway gives rise to magnetic fields due to the flow of traction currents to and from trainsets and these fields can couple with external equipment to produce electrical interference. The major area of concern is the interference of telecommunication circuits, especially where these are parallel to the tracks. This problem is of growing importance and significance due to the explosion of interest in electrical and electronic equipment for both business and entertainment use. Railways control the magnitude of much of the external fields by use of booster transformers which are 1:1 current transformers. These are spaced at intervals of 3.2 km along the railway and the primary winding of the transformer is connected in series with the catenary system whilst the secondary winding is connected in series with a return conductor. Transformer action forces a current to flow in the return conductor which is equal in magnitude but which flows in the opposite direction to the catenary current. The return conductor is then connected to the rails midway between booster transformers and this has the effect of 'sucking' the return current out of the rails and earth and placing it into the return conductor. The return conductor is located close to the catenary system so that the two magnetic fields partly cancel and therefore reduce the external field generated by the railway.

9.9 DC low voltage systems

In the UK, low voltage DC electrification has been adopted for many of the services of the former Southern Region of British Rail and for the whole of the London Underground. The Docklands Light Railway in London also uses DC supply for traction.

Both BR and DLR use a single positive conductor rail at track level positioned just outside the running rails, with the running rails themselves being used for 'negative' return. London Underground however uses a positive conductor rail placed to one side of the running rails with a separate negative conductor rail running down the centre of the track.

A description of conductor rails, insulators and other fastenings for both systems is included in Chapter 5 on Track.

9.10 AC power distribution for DC systems

DC electrification requires the provision of two separate electrical power distribution systems. An AC three-phase distribution system is required to distribute power from the national grid supply points or the railway authority generating station to each traction sub station. At each traction, sub station

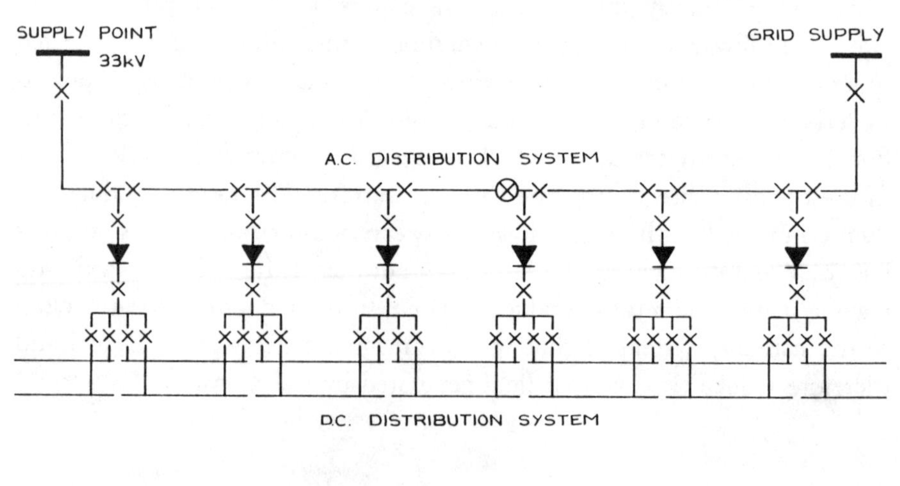

Fig. 9.3. AC and DC distribution on a DC system.

located along the railway, transformation and rectification to DC takes place and the power is then fed direct to local current rails. The AC distribution system transmits the high voltage supply to each sub station by means of a lineside cable 'main' which is continuous between two supply points. A circuit breaker is provided at each sub station for each incoming and outgoing cable and for each rectifer.

Under normal conditions, a single circuit breaker is located approximately midway between the supply points maintained in the open position and the sub station is supplied only from the nearest supply point. Under failure conditions, all sub stations can obtain power from either of the two supply points.

The design of the AC distribution system must therefore be such that the total power requirement of the sub station can be transmitted from either of the two adjacent supply points. The choice of distribution voltage depends upon this total power requirement and the distance between suitable supply points.

The use of higher voltages reduces the current drawn from the system thereby reducing power system losses and voltage reduction, allowing greater distances between supply points. However, systems at lower voltages have lower equipment costs but will either require features to compensate for voltage drops or necessitate supplies to be taken more frequently along the route.

9.11 DC Power distribution

Figure 9.3 shows the relationship between the AC and DC distribution systems on a railway using DC traction supply.

The DC power distribution system between the sub station and the conductor rails must be designed to fulfil the following basic requirements:

- To allow peak accelerating current to be taken by trains at any location.
- To provide an average voltage at any train sufficient for the train timetable to be achieved.
- To allow maintenance outages of equipment without affecting the ability of trains to maintain time table.

- To enable the train service to be maintained under power distribution equipment failure conditions.

All DC track sections are usually double end fed from adjacent locations in order to provide the required level of security and the necessary train voltages. All DC circuit breakers are normally maintained in the closed position. Because of the electrical resistance of the conductor rails, it is the spacing between sub stations that dictates the voltage at the train.

The most economic DC distribution system is achieved with the greatest spacing between sub stations which will still be able to maintain the required voltage for the train. Typically sub stations are spaced at intervals along the track of not less than 4 km or more than 7 km depending upon the maximum loading in peak periods.

9.12 The effects of electrification

Many railways around the world have been converted from other forms of motive power to electrification in recent decades. Trends indicate that this is likely to continue for the foreseeable future.

Experience of the effects of electrification on other engineering disciplines and operational aspects is now considerable and must not be overlooked when considering such a fundamental change.

Most of the serious effects relate to overhead AC electrification and this is the system now generally favoured for modern conversion where no other system pre-exists.

Any railway authority considering such a major change needs to address the following subjects:

- Structural modifications required for over bridges to give adequate clearances.
- Increased height requirements for footbridge and other parapets to provide safe protection.
- Increased standards for lineside fencing to further restrict trespass, particularly if conductor rails are at ground level.

- Increased protection against potential danger from cranes and other mobile plant working alongside the tracks and overhead electrical equipment.
- Increased protection to staff working on or about the railway.
- The effect on other electrical equipment and systems such as track circuits, signalling, telephones, computers, CCTV etc.

9.13 Inspection and maintenance

As in any other part of the railway infrastructure, maintenance of all the equipment associated with railway electrification is essential if the service is to be properly sustained.

Each railway authority needs to set up a separate organisation to inspect and maintain all the electrical equipment, both within buildings and outside on, alongside and over the tracks. Standard electrical equipment needs to be inspected as laid down by Regulations by suitably qualified and experienced staff in that field. There are however other components which are outside the strictly electrical engineer's field and these too need specialist inspection.

Components that come under this category include the following:

- Overhead structures and catenary anchors.
- Foundations for masts/portals.
- Cable runs and their supporting structures.
- Cable ducts, troughs and sub-ways.
- Electrical bonds to conductor and running rails.

It should also be recognised that electrification brings a new dimension to all operating staff and to those whose duties require them to be about the railway. All staff must be properly trained in relation to safe procedures that must be taken for carrying out work and in the event of accident or other incident. Apparently simple duties like cleaning signal lenses, lopping tree branches or painting station canopies, take on new risks when energised overhead electrical equipment is present.

CHAPTER 10

Signalling and Train Control

10.1 The early history of railway signalling

From the very beginning of railways, it was soon realised that some form of signalling to control the movement and speed of trains is necessary if there is to be any degree of safety from collision. Even before the introduction of steam locomotives, when horses were the most common means of providing haulage power, accidents were prone to happen on tramways because of the difficulty of providing enough brake power to overcome the inertia of a train of heavily loaded vehicles. Once locomotives were introduced with more power, higher speeds and longer trains behind, stopping became even more difficult and hazardous.

Because of this, it quickly became obvious that some means of signalling was necessary to indicate to a locomotive driver, well in advance, whether he needed to slow down and stop his train under controlled braking or could proceed at speed.

In the early days, each railway company employed men called policemen who were posted at stations, junctions and other important places such as level crossings, to control the running of trains. Initially they signalled to the drivers using hand signals. These early policemen were organised very similarly to the Metropolitan Police and their duties included keeping general law and order on railway premises and removal of trespassers as well as operating points and signalling trains.

There was no means of communication between individual policemen controlling trains who allowed trains to pass on the rash assumption that if enough time had elapsed since the previous train then the line was likely to be clear!

With this primitive type of control, accidents were not as frequent as one might expect but when they did occur they were sometimes very serious and caused casualties.

By the middle of the nineteenth century, many railway companies had developed some form of fixed signal to replace hand signals and some grouping of signal and point levers in a common 'frame' was seen. This was the forerunner of the signal box. In 1860 the first installation in which levers were interlocked so that signals could not be 'cleared' until points were properly set, was brought into service.

This principle of interlocking has remained with railways ever since and is fundamental to the safety of any signalling and train control system.

Another such principle became known as 'fail-safe' and this too had to be learned in the hard school of experience. Originally fixed signals had to be turned or moved in some way to indicate a clear road. Because of a number of accidents with this type of arrangement, it soon became apparent that signals could stick in the clear position or wires could break without the possibility of turning the signal to the danger position. Following this all semaphore signals were designed to have counterbalance weights which returned the signal to a 'danger' position in the event of failure of any components.

These two principles of interlocking and fail-safe remain today and are fundamental to the safe operation of all signal equipment and systems.

The other great need in early railways was to have some form of communication between signal boxes. Again by about 1860 a simple method of indicating that a train was 'on line' or 'clear was invented giving this vital link for the first time. The system was made possible by an arrangement of electro-magnets with a low current passing through to indicate by a needle whether or not a train was still on the line between the boxes or had passed to the next section of a track. This was a tremendous step forward and removed for good the danger of a broken down train blocking the path of the next train which was signalled through on the assumption that sufficient time had elapsed for the road to be clear.

Fig. 10.1. Semaphore signals.

10.2 Modern signalling principles

All modern signalling systems have the following six basic objectives:

- To control trains in a safe manner for the conditions ahead.
- To maintain a safe distance to any train ahead or dead end ahead.
- To prevent the setting of conflicting movements.
- To ensure that points are locked in the correct position.
- To enable trains to operate to the headway required.
- To enable trains to operate to the scheduled speed with minimum disruption consistent with safety.

By far the most dangerous movement of trains is when passing over points and crossings. It is vital that trains are kept from moving into any position of danger and are only allowed to proceed when all train movements are properly co-ordinated and when the route ahead is properly set and clear.

The spacing of signals depends to a large extent on the minimum time interval that is required between trains, known as the headway. On a main line railway where mixed stock passes at different speeds, spacing of signals becomes a complex subject. On rapid transit railways and light railway systems it becomes more straightforward as the trains tend to have the same movement characteristics.

Once signal boxes had a positive means of knowing whether or not sections of track were definitely clear of trains, it was possible to introduce what became known as the 'block system'. The specified lengths of line between boxes, stations or junctions, termed block sections, formed a space interval between trains. The block system principle, which states that not more than one train should be allowed on one line in a block section, was established, a principle that continues to be the basis of modern signalling today.

10.3 Track circuits

The simplest and most effective way of detecting that there is no train on a particular length of track is by the use of the track circuit which is shown in diagrammatic form in Fig. 10.2 below.

In this simple arrangement, the current flows from the battery to the relay through the rails and the green light is operated from the relay. When an approaching train reaches the section, the axles short circuit the current

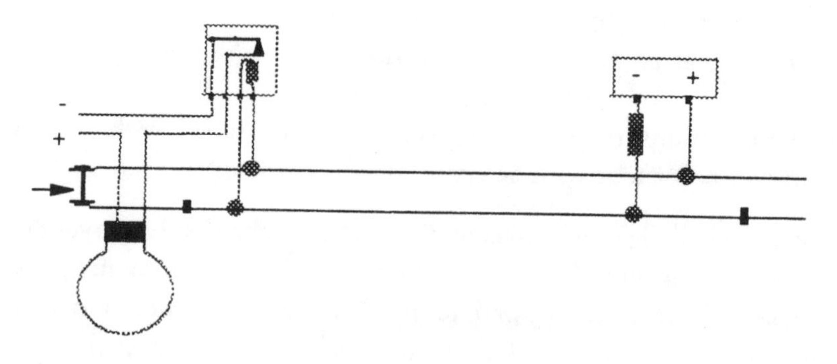

Fig. 10.2. The DC track circuit.

from the relay which then drops and the green light goes out and a red light comes on, fed from the relay contact.

This is a 'fail-safe' arrangement as if the battery goes flat, a rail breaks or a contact becomes loose etc, the result is the green light goes out and the red light comes on.

10.4 Point operation, locking and detection

As has been stated previously, movements over points and crossings are the most dangerous and therefore point equipment requires the most built-in safeguards. The potential hazards to safe operation from points arise from the possibility that they will be set in the wrong direction or that they will come open during the passage of a train.

To prevent points coming open, they are locked in position for a facing move and to ensure that the train is not allowed to proceed over them until they are safe, they are 'detected' to be in the correct position, fully 'home' and locked.

The lock is held until it is proved that there is no train passing over the points by means of the track circuits, and is applied from the moment that a train approaches to within its braking distance of the toe of the points. This is to prevent a signal man from moving the points after a train has accepted a signal.

Points on early railways were operated by hand worked levers, usually close to the points themselves. Later, they were still hand operated but the levers were more remote from the points and grouped into frames, along

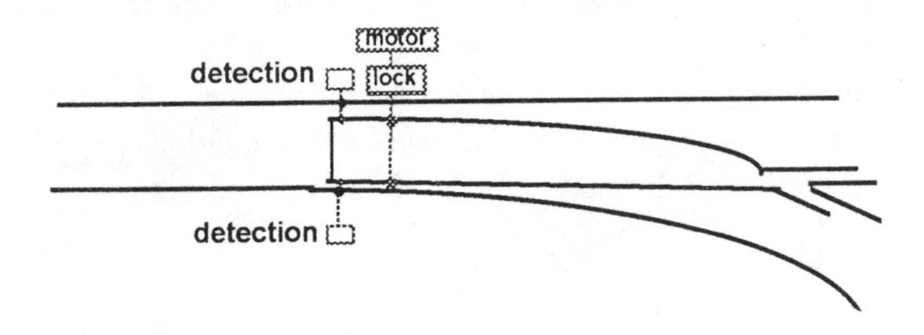

Fig. 10.3. Diagram showing point locking and detection.

with signal levers. Considerable skill and strength was required to 'throw' point levers that were some distance from the points because of the friction and inertia to be overcome.

Although some points in depots and sidings continue to be hand worked, most modern railways now use some form of motor to move points from one position to another. These motors are usually electrically driven but can be driven by compressed air, as on the London Underground.

With modern point motor assemblies, devices are integrated into the mechanism which will lock the points in position once they are fully home and will also electrically detect that they are actually fully closed. They have the added advantage of being able to detect the presence of an obstruction, such as a discarded can, in the point blades.

10.5 Interlocking

The interlocking of signals and points is another principle born out of hard experience in the early days, which is now universally adopted. In essence interlocking is introduced to prevent signal men accidentally clearing a signal before points are properly set or clearing signals that would allow a conflicting movement. In manual boxes, a series of sliding bars is connected to the levers. These bars have notches and dogs in them which will only allow operation of the signals in correct relationship to other signals and when relevant points are correctly set.

Similar devices are incorporated into power operated boxes which follow the same principles and prevent operation of signals or points for conflicting moves. Similarly signals cannot be cleared in areas of pointwork until the correct route is set and all trains are clear.

From the foregoing, it can be seen that railway signalling is basically simple and can be made absolutely fail-safe for all conditions providing the following three basic sub-systems are in place and working:

- Track circuits
- Point locking and detection
- Interlocking

10.6 Minimum headways

The headway of a particular train service is the minimum time interval that can be run between trains. The most critical point in this consideration is at a station because the station stop or dwell time must be taken into account. The practical minimum dwell time at any station will vary considerably and will depend upon the number of passengers alighting and getting on, the number and spacing of doors on the rolling stock, width of platform, the number of waiting passengers obstructing movement, the proportion of passengers carrying luggage and the percentage of passengers who are familiar daily commuters.

Typical dwell times at busy Metro stations might be expected to be about half a minute reducing on some light rail systems to as little as twenty seconds. Main line semi-fast commuter services at intermediate stops would probably have a station dwell time of at least a minute.

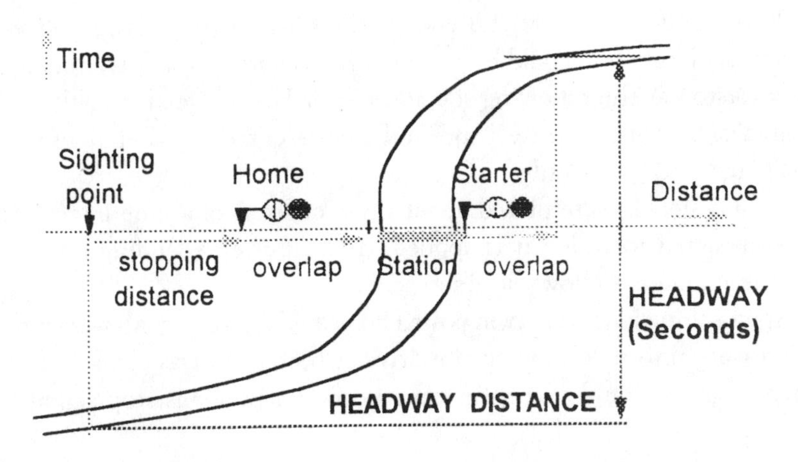

Fig. 10.4. Headway distance and time.

Headway is measured from the time at which the driver reaches the sighting point of the first signal to a point at which the tail of the train clears the overlap of the signal ahead.

10.7 Home and distant signals

As trains began to travel faster towards the second half of the nineteenth century, another problem arose with the early semaphore signal systems. This related to the distance ahead that, an engine driver could be expected to see a signal that was at danger. On a train travelling at say 40 mph, a driver would have to react quite quickly to bring his train to a halt at a danger signal even if he could see that signal half a mile away. At double that speed, he still would only have the same viewing distance of a danger signal but to try and stop in such a short distance would at the very least be very uncomfortable, cause damage to the train or the track and might even cause derailment.

To give early warning of signals at danger therefore, all signals were classed as either 'home' or 'distant'. On running main lines, all stop or home signals were provided with a distant signal in advance which indicated whether or not the following home signal was clear. When using semaphore signals, the arms of the distant signals were usually painted yellow with a black vee and notched at the end. Distant signals had green and yellow (or amber) lenses and could be passed only at caution, the driver being then ready to stop at the following signal. Stop or Home signals usually had red painted arms with a white band and square cut ends, their lenses being always red and green only.

Distant signals were placed about three quarters of a mile in advance of the stop signal to which it is applied, the distance depending on gradient and the maximum allowable line speed.

Approaching junctions, twin posted home and distant signals were provided which were thus able to warn the driver which path was clear. Very often distant signals would share the same post as a previous stop signal.

10.8 Subsidiary signals

Subsidiary signals are used for controlling low speed shunting and other non-running movements both on main lines and in yards. These signals are usually small and at ground level and can allow shunting movements on the main line, calling-on signals for coupling up locomotives to trains and working in the reverse direction to normal. Where signals are difficult to see because of obstructions or tight curves, repeater signals can be provided to overcome that difficulty.

10.9 Two aspect colour light signalling

Manually operated systems of signalling and point operation continued well into the twentieth century on most main line railways in the UK. However, when DC electrification began to be installed, semaphore signalling began to be replaced by electrically powered colour lights. On the London Underground, those sections which were electrified, notable the 'tube' lines, were also signalled electrically.

The most simple system of electric signalling is to have signals with two lamps each with a fixed coloured lens, red or green for a stop or home signal, and orange or green for a repeater or distant signal.

On rapid transit, metro and light rail systems, two aspect signalling is usually adopted because the braking distances are short due to low speeds

Fig. 10.5. Two aspect signalling.

and high braking rates, hence the distance needed for the driver to stop the train is usually such as to be able to see the signal in time. Where this is not the case, a repeater signal is placed in front on the running signal to give advanced warning.

For main line railways, when two aspect signalling is used, a distant signal is positioned in front of the running signal, in very much the same way as was for semaphore signalling.

The initial cost of installing colour light signalling is high but the advantages are considerable. Pulling signal and point levers by hand was a skilful but heavy task and severely limited the distances that signal boxes could be apart. Once points and signals were operated electrically, the number of signal boxes could be reduced dramatically and much longer lengths of railway could be controlled from one point.

10.10 Three aspect colour light signalling

Where train speeds are higher, or headways are closer, three aspect signalling can be used. This allows trains to approach closer and effectively combines

Fig. 10.6. Three aspect signalling

the distant signal of the signal ahead with the running signal. These signals show red, yellow or green indications, corresponding to the night-time red and yellow, green and yellow or double green indications of the semaphore stop signal with a distant beneath it. In colour light signalling, the terms distant and home signal no longer apply as every signal has this dual function, depending where the trains are located at any particular time.

10.11 Four aspect colour light signalling

Since the middle of the twentieth century, most new signalling installations on high speed railways in the UK have been four aspect. With three aspect signalling there is a limitation on the minimum spacing of signals since all signals act as both stop and distant. Signals have to be about three quarters of a mile apart where line speeds are at a maximum to allow an adequate braking distance to be maintained. This has the effect of keeping trains about two miles apart before being checked.

The four aspect system allows trains at higher speeds to slow down earlier and hence to get closer to the train ahead in a controlled manner.

Reading from the top down, the four aspects are yellow, green, yellow and red. The advantage with having red at the bottom is that it can be placed at driver's eye level and there is no lens hood below it which might assist snow to build up and obscure the light. It is a 'fail-safe' principle that maintenance of a red light must take precedence over everything else.

The sequence of four aspect signalling is as follows:

Green – Continue at full speed.
Double yellow – Proceed at caution, reduce power, perhaps with some braking depending on type and speed of train.
Single Yellow – Power off, controlled braking.
Red – Stop.

As can be seen from Fig. 10.7 below, signals can be spaced closer together with this system and headway times can be shorter, as trains are subject to more control.

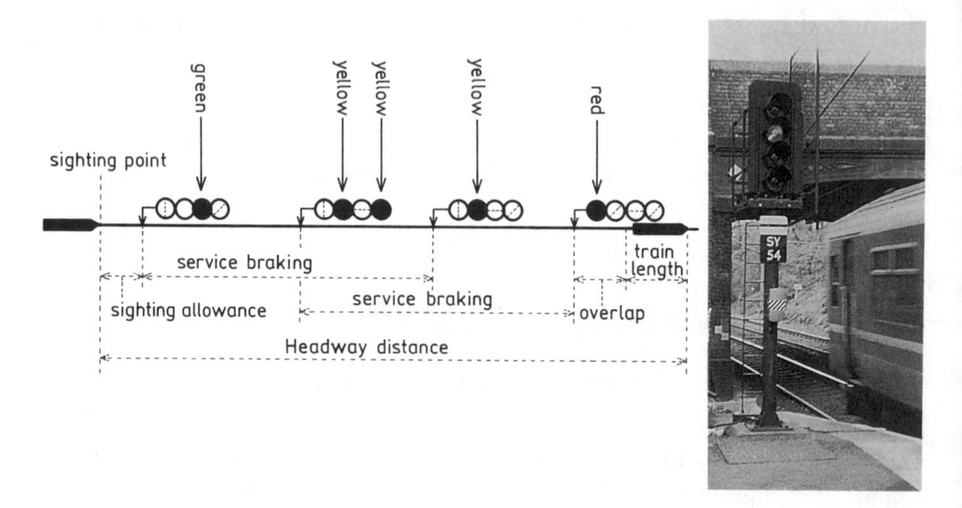

Fig. 10.7. Four aspect signalling.

Unlike semaphore signals, colour light signals at junctions do not usually have separate signals for each route ahead. There is normally a single signal with, above it, a route indicator consisting of three or more white lights in a diagonal line at 45° on each side of the vertical, illuminated according to whichever route is set and clear. Sometimes, at complicated junctions or at terminal stations, signals indicate a 'theatre' type or dot matrix illuminated number showing the line or platform number for which the route is set.

At most facing junctions, a speed restriction is placed on the diverging route, and when points are set for the diverging route the signal ahead of the junction will show a single yellow even when the route is clear of trains. Only when the approaching train has passed this signal and been slowed by it, will the signal at the junction itself clear.

It can be seen from the foregoing that multiple aspect signalling can be extremely effective in controlling trains both on busy plain line and at junctions and termini.

10.12 Transmission based signalling

The arrival of the micro chip and computers has revolutionised railway signalling in recent decades. There are now in existence many systems around the world where trains are controlled by computer, including keeping trains on schedule as well as ensuring that there is complete safety and protection to all train movements.

Present and future generations of signalling will use computers extensively to enable trains to be controlled in a closed loop system. Each train is constantly updated from the trackside computer with the maximum safe speed and distance that it can go and in turn tells the trackside its own position and speed. Some metro and light rail systems have introduced automatic running of trains between stations and such ATO needs to be compatible with the computer controlled signalling and safety systems.

These combining systems are often known as Automatic Train Operation (ATO), Automatic Train Scheduling (ATS), and Automatic Train Protection (ATP). Absolute compatibility is essential and needs to be checked rigourously.

On such automatic systems, the principles of signalling must still be rigidly applied if safety is to be maintained. Interlocking of points, signals and routes is still a very important requirement to ensure that trains only operate when it is safe to do so.

The main benefits of the use of computers are the reduction in the number of trackside components and the faster recovery from disruption due to the ability to communicate safety information to the train on a continuous basis. Experience has shown that computer control systems need extensive testing after installation before trains can be confidently operated. A period of several months must be built in to any 'critical path' programme to ensure that such testing/commissioning is carried out thoroughly, if early problems are to be kept to an absolute minimum.

In operation, the trackside computer sends messages to the train telling it the value and position of speed restrictions and track gradients ahead and imposes a zero speed restriction at such a point as to protect the train ahead. The train computer then calculates a target speed and distance from this information, with a safety margin built in to take account of variations such as adhesion characteristics due to weather. The train then monitors itself to ensure that it runs within the maximum speed envelope such that it will stop in time whilst running at the performance level required by the automatic train operation commands. The train also transmits back its speed and position so that other trains can be kept at a suitable distance.

In addition to this, the trackside computer also monitors that the train is operating within the safe speed and sends an emergency brake message if it does not.

To protect against the loss of information, should the train fail to receive a constant stream of valid messages it will apply its emergency brakes.

10.13 Proof of safety and safety standards

Signalling has now advanced from the position when proof of safety mainly relied on demonstration that components and the system as a whole would always be 'fail safe'.

With modern systems, it is necessary to show that the whole railway system is designed, built, installed, operated and maintained in a safe manner. This requires that any new design is rigourously carried out and demonstrated to be able to meet the specified level of safety and the application of the system must also be proven to be correct.

The component parts of any signalling and control system must each meet the required the safety level depending on the likely results of failure. For instance, the level of safety required for a component, the failure of which could lead to death, must be of a higher standard than for a component or system, the failure of which could cause people to be misled into a dangerous situation.

Proof of safety and compliance with safety standards needs to be applied to all signal and control equipment, both hardware and software, system design, testing, commissioning, maintenance and replacement.

Formal proof of safety techniques must include detailed consideration of all the possible effects of each possible hardware and software failure. This enables calculation to be made of the mathematical probability of such a failure occurring. In addition, consideration is to be given to the possible action that can be taken when incidents/breakdowns occur. This will highlight possible weaknesses and enable measures to be introduced to prevent matters leading to unacceptable hazards.

Railway signalling and train control is a complex and rapidly changing subject. Those wishing to obtain more detailed information are advised to read the following:

L T C Holt, *Red for Danger*.
O S Nock, *Railway Signalling* (A&C Black)
Kichenside and Kichenside, *British Railway Signalling* (Ian Allan Ltd).
The Institution of Railway Signal Engineers Proceedings.

CHAPTER 11

Systems and Communications

11.1 Getting things done!

In this book, so far we have concentrated largely on the material things which together make up a railway. We have considered how they have evolved thus far, how they perform, how they interelate, how they degenerate and how they are eventually replaced.

Understandably, engineers in all disciplines tend to concentrate on their particular area of the material components, perhaps sometimes giving less attention to non-material considerations.

This chapter therefore looks at the 'people' aspects of railway engineering, including systems of working and means of communicating between people both within the railway organisation and to passengers and the world at large outside.

Systems engineering looks at the whole process that is involved in producing something. To make any progress, it is necessary to break down the complete system under consideration into its component parts (subsystems) and then to examine each in turn, breaking down further until the required degree of simplicity has been obtained.

However, just looking at the various component parts will not enable the whole system to function. To achieve this, each part must 'talk' to one another. The path by which this occurs provides the interface between two subsystems. Identification of these interfaces is crucial to the system as a whole.

It is in this area that humans tend to be the weakest. In particular, the interface between human processes and between human and machine actions are where most errors are introduced.

11.2 Human processes

In human processes, a useful way of looking at what happens is to consider as well as the various inputs that feed into the process and the outputs that are expected, any constraints and supporting services that are needed.

Such an approach helps understanding of the way that the process can be executed and, by identifying the necessary inputs, constraints and supports, forces the system designer to consider all the factors that lead to outputs.

On early railways, many systems were introduced informally as experience was gained, to fulfil certain basic engineering functions. Often where railways were simple or limited in layout and unsophisticated technically, one man or group of men would be responsible for most aspects of one basic component or part of the infrastructure and there was no need to work out a system as such.

A good example of this would be the permanent way lengthman or 'ganger' who would know his length of track intimately. He would also consider that it was his job to walk the track, inspect it, carry out daily adjustment, repair locally and replace broken components when he deemed it necessary.

As time went by however, many such functions began to be carried out by different individuals and even by different organisations. In the case under consideration, track inspection, day-to-day maintenance and track renewal over the whole of a railway layout might be carried out by different organisations with different plant available. In that case, a system needs to be devised with proper communication between parties.

11.3 Good feedback

The simplest systems have a process that acts upon the input and produces an output according to a set procedure. Such systems only work if completely

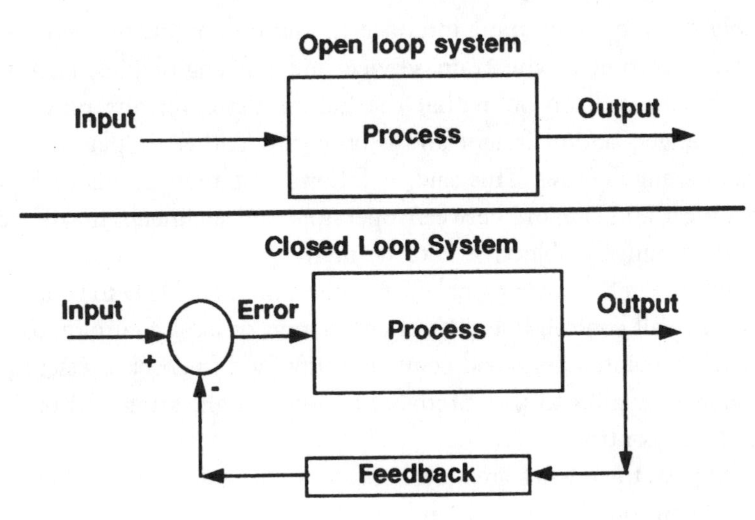

Fig. 11.1. Open and closed loop systems.

mechanistic as the output will differ according to any change in the process or any disturbance to the process from outside. By constantly comparing the output with the desired state, any error can be detected and put right. This feedback of what is happening enables the process to be self controlling.

An understanding of the nature of feedback is essential to predict the effects that it will have. Although theoretically better than open loop systems, if the nature, timing or amount of feedback is wrong then the result can be to over correct the error.

It is important to remember these simple facts when designing control systems. A good example of this is that of a railway controller operating with poor communications. If the situation being described to him does not reflect reality, either because the observer is only seeing part of the picture, or is exaggerating the true position, or even if the time that the message has taken to reach the controller is such that the situation has then changed, then the action that he takes may well be less than the best and possibly even make the situation worse.

11.4 Interface between operation and engineering

Probably the most important interface in any railway organisation is that between operation of the train service and the engineering back-up. It cannot be stressed too often that the 'raison d'etre' for any railway is to carry passengers and/or freight and is primarily neither to 'play trains' nor to practice engineering. This said, it follows that there needs to be close co-operation and support between operators and engineers in all areas if the primary railway objective is to be met.

Within the railway operational organisation, there are likely to be interfaces between overall control, line control and station or local control and, as has been already pointed out, good communication and feedback is essential.

The same applies to the interfaces between engineering and operation at all of the control levels.

In the past, there was a great deal of face-to-face informal communication between men 'on the ground' and problems were often solved locally by individuals who knew and respected one another. In the days when local manual signal boxes were close to stations and shunters' and trackmen's cabins, individuals would quite often meet in the box and agree action that should be taken, as and when the need arose. In this local arrangement, the interfaces between operating and engineering were usually adequately covered. There is one word of warning however, that must always be kept in mind when extolling the virtues of local face-to-face problem solving. Local problems may well have wider effects and the best overall solution may be different from the one that only deals with the local situation.

As railways have become less labour intensive however, and control more centralised, local interfaces have become more remote and good means of communication therefore become even more critical. This communication must be both horizontal, to all parties at the same level, and vertical, to other levels of control.

11.5 Interface between operator and user

Communication with the passenger or customer is also very important so that they may be kept aware of the situation and appraised of any likely variation to the service for which they have paid and can rightly expect to receive.

11.6 The railway systems pyramid

Control of a modern railway can be seen as a pyramid of systems.

The signalling system extends from the train to the trackside and to the central control room. Similarly the other systems that assist in controlling the railway and informing/directing passengers or customers can be thought of as part of this pyramid of control. Each system is an integral part of the control of a railway and consists of equipment and operators, the material and human aspects of control. Backing each operational system is the engineering required, including the vital maintenance, fault finding and central diagnostics that is an essential part of the on-going engineering service.

All the various systems that work together to control a railway system, and ensure the best possible service, have both interactive and automatic

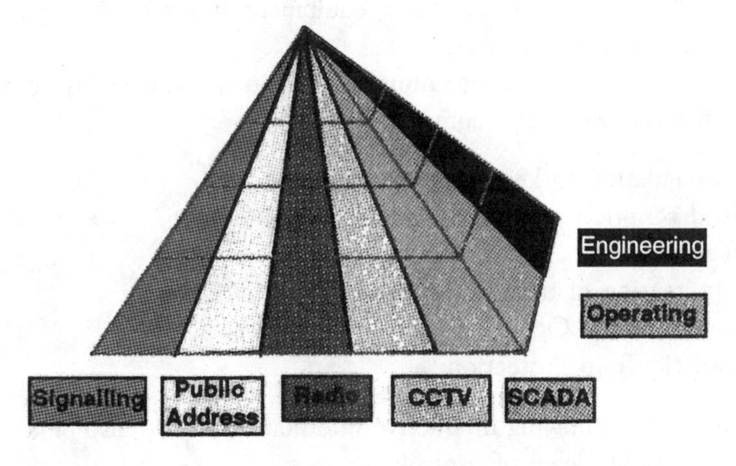

Fig. 11.2. The systems pyramid.

effects on the railway system as a whole. These effects can be obvious, formal and immediate but many others may be less obvious and will take time to make their effect known.

A good example of the latter is bridge inspection. If bridges are not inspected properly, then some essential maintenance may not be picked up and conditions could deteriorate. However, a perfectly good service could continue to run and it might be years before conditions degenerate to such an extent that services are effected.

The main systems that need to be put into operation, which directly affect and assist the day-to-day operation, will include those listed in the following sections. Each railway must also ensure that adequate systems are put into practice in all other areas to ensure trouble-free operation in the longer term.

11.7 The railway signalling system

To be able to safely and efficiently control any railway, there must be an adequate signalling system. The technical details and evolution of railway signalling is covered in Chapter 10 of this book.

In basic terms, railway signalling has two prime functions. These are firstly a means of control of the railway and secondly a means of providing operational information to locations, equipment and individuals to enable appropriate action to be taken.

A fully comprehensive signalling system on a complex layout should provide the following data automatically:

- Train regulation to keep within timetables.
- Train description and route setting.
- Staff protection.
- Full protection of train movements.
- Automatic Train Operation } when installed
- Automatic Train Protection }

With these, the following interactive information should also be available to the appropriate level of control:

- Information about service disruption.
- Train service reports, history/graphing.
- Early prediction of possible problems and operational conflicts.
- Train and crew positions.
- Arrival time predictions.
- Local data on signals and speed codes.

Each railway operational organisation will need to agree, with its engineering back-up, the levels at which this automatic and interactive information is to be provided and at what level appropriate action will be taken. The means of control will vary widely from a timetable modification, which could affect a whole line, to a local route modification only affecting two sets of points.

11.8 The public address system

Once potential passengers enter railway property, the railway authority has a duty of care towards them to ensure, as far as possible, that they travel safely and reach the destination for which they have paid their fare.

The various stages of this process including where and how to purchase a ticket, what route to take to which platform and where to alight, can usually be covered by fixed notices, maps, platform indicators and other publicity.

From the earliest days of railways however, it was found that it is essential also to have some means of communicating with passengers before and during their journeys. Perhaps the most frustrating experience for any passenger is to enter an unfamiliar environment and not be able to find out where to go for the train or, having found the right platform, to be unsure which train is the correct one.

Almost as bad is an inefficient, echoing or otherwise inaudible public address system which only confuses or frustrates rather than giving clear understandable information.

On any modern railway system, whether it is main line, suburban, metro or light rail, there must be an efficient and audible public address system. At the planning stage of any new railway or large interchange station this subject needs to have the very careful consideration of both the operators and the engineers concerned.

Experience has shown that in large public areas, it is far better to have a large number of small speakers placed at a fairly low level than a smaller number of high level or high powered speakers.

Good public address facilities enable network-wide messages to be sent from a network control centre, a line control office or just to passengers on one station or platform either from the centre or from the local station control.

Public address systems are the principle means of controlling passengers and should be used on platforms and circulating areas to control passenger flow, assist train boarding and evacuation when emergencies occur.

These facilities are absolutely crucial in dealing with any emergency and railway authorities should consider carefully what arrangements should be made for automatic pre-recorded instructions for evacuation if there is no response from control rooms or local operators, in the event of fire being detected.

Discussion between the railway authority and local emergency services for dealing with such emergencies should include the proposed use and control of all public address systems.

11.9 Telephones and radio

Voice contact by telephone has become so much part of our ordinary working, family and leisure lives that it is hard for us now to imagine how people managed without it.

It is well, however, to remember that passenger railways had been operating successfully for almost half a century before Graham Bell's new telephone began to be accepted as a reliable means of communication. Electric telegraph, in various forms, began to be used to a limited extent on some railways from the 1850's, but this was a slow letter-by-letter method of transmitting messages often based on the Morse Code which was not known to all railway men.

By 1860, this cumbersome method gave place to a simplified system in which an electro-magnet could hold a single steel needle deflected to right or left pointing to an indication 'line clear' or 'train on line'. If no current was passed to the instrument, the needle would remain vertical indicating 'line blocked', thus making the system 'fail-safe'.

With the introduction of this simple electro-magnetic system, the first instant communication between signal boxes became possible and the 'block telegraph system' was established. Telephones with hand cranked bells were installed later but were not considered 'fail-safe' and were an additional aid to the signal man rather than a replacement for the block telegraph instruments and bells used to communicate the position of trains from box to box.

Today, telephones are used extensively to communicate information throughout a railway system and to the passengers and other customers. Consideration needs to be given to security of supply to important telephones, particularly, if they are provided by an outside telephone authority. Alternative lines supplied from a separate power source should be provided in all control rooms and other vital control locations both linking with each other and with the emergency services.

The possibility of an incident on a railway severing power and telephone cables needs to be addressed. Some degree of protection in this respect can be given by ensuring that power, signal and telephone cables are sited in different cable runs and ducts, preferably on different sides of the track or tunnel.

Most railways have an extensive internal telephone system with telephones in all control rooms, signal boxes, station operations rooms, on each platform and at many signals. However, those working on or about the railway are often remote from telephones and, before radio, had to walk long distances to report incidents, progress on works or give up possession.

Radio is now the principal means of communication and control for those staff who cannot easily get to a telephone.

Radio is used as a means of communicating with train drivers and increasingly, with station staff, police, ambulance and other emergency services.

The use of 'pagers' and other personal radio communication links can be invaluable in contacting 'on call' and other key personnel when incidents occur.

It is vital to ensure that all radio systems used by the railway and emergency services are compatible and that the various command and control structures can communicate in all eventualities and operational locations.

11.10 Closed circuit television

CCTV provides a very useful feedback mechanism enabling control rooms and the emergency services to gauge what is happening on the ground.

In particular, CCTV enables controllers at stations to manage flow of passengers and to prevent dangerous overcrowding situations to develop. By introducing video recorders, CCTV enables analysis of events which can lead to future improvements. In the event of crime being committed, it can also prove extremely useful in detection and obtaining prosecutions.

CCTV on platforms enables drivers to see passenger movement onto and off trains and to decide when doors may be safely closed.

On unmanned stations, CCTV cameras on platforms, by ticket machines and at other strategic viewing locations enable close scrutiny of passenger movements from the control room. In conjunction with the use of the public address system, this can be a very powerful tool in dealing with vandalism and other misbehaviour. CCTV has been particularly useful on light rail systems with frequent unmanned stops.

With a complex system and large interchange stations, the task of watching a large number of CCTV monitors becomes at the same time daunting and very boring. Much care needs to be given to the arrangement of this in the control room to ensure that the best use of the equipment is made both during normal working and at the time of incidents. As has been said previously, the interface between the machine and human intervention is the weakest and needs to be addressed if the full potential of the 'hardware' is to be realised.

11.11 Equipment operation and system maintenance

Traditionally, on most railways the responsibility for the maintenance of fixed engineering equipment on railways has been left with the relevant engineering departments. Bound up with this has been first hand knowledge of the state and operational mode of various pieces of equipment. Generally this has worked reasonably well, but it can lead to frustration on the part of an operator faced with a crisis situation if he is unable to reach the 'man who knows'.

Increasingly, systems are being introduced on modern railways to monitor the operation of critical parts of the railway equipment infrastructure. The objective of this is not in any way to move responsibility for maintaining equipment from the right quarter but to give information to both operating control rooms and engineers to enable them to make rapid decisions when incidents arise. This is particularly important when unexpected things happen which could develop into a life threatening situation.

In particular, the hazards of fire, smoke and flooding are influenced by the operation of certain critical pieces of equipment, including the following:

- Escalators and lifts
- Pumps
- Sump level indicators/cut-outs
- Fans and louvres
- Automatic alarm systems
- Flood containment doors and barriers

Monitoring should indicate at all times whether or not each piece of equipment is actually working and in what mode (e.g. up or down, pressure or exhaust) and if not working, whether or not it is capable of working or is down for maintenance.

In the case of a train on fire producing dense smoke in a tunnel, for instance, the Controller needs to know quickly the mode of operation of any fans in nearby vent shafts before deciding which way to detrain any passengers in other stranded trains.

A co-ordinated approach is needed to keep all these various systems running. Ideally everything from the state of the train equipment to the preventative maintenance of an escalator should be visible to the maintainer and his manager.

Especially in the case of an emergency, the quality, accuracy and promptness of the information given will largely determine the quality of the response and the resultant 'down time' of the railway.

CHAPTER 12

Lifts, Escalators and Pumps

12.1 Vertical transportation

With any passenger railway system, there is always necessity for passengers to either climb or be carried in the vertical dimension, over or under the tracks to interchange to another line or mode or to leave or enter the system. This applies to surface railways, underground and elevated railways whether they are main line, metro or, to a lesser extent light rail.

In Chapter 2 of this book, dealing with the design of station layout, the subject of when escalators are required rather than fixed stairs is covered in paragraph 2.11. There is also some reference in this chapter on provision of lifts for disabled and mobility impaired passengers.

In practice, when designing new railways, any height to be negotiated of 5 m or more in busy stations should be provided with an escalator, at least in the upwards direction. Anything in excess of 6 m, whether up or down should have escalator provision, even in outer area or less busy stations.

12.2 The development of early lifts

Lifts (or elevators) have existed in one form or another almost since the invention of the wheel, which must have been closely followed by the idea of adding a rope and bucket to make a simple hoist. The main concern with this early form of vertical transport was the tendency for the rope to wear and then break without warning under the heaviest loads, thus making it unfavoured for carrying people or livestock!

During the 1830's and 1840's water hydraulics began to be widely used for hoisting devices, cranes and lifting platforms.

In the last two decades of the nineteenth century, rope suspended lifts began to become popular. This was largely because of the manufacture of steel wire ropes of consistent quality and the invention of automatic safety gear which would prevent the falling of a lift car if the suspension ropes should break.

Since the 1950's, hydraulic lifts have made a limited come-back in certain well-defined areas, mainly for small lifts for disabled passengers travelling only up and down small to medium heights.

The main disadvantage with lifts is they encourage bunching of passengers waiting for the lift car to arrive and similarly generate flow peaks at the exit points. Another disadvantage is when they breakdown between floors, the freeing of passengers can be difficult and time consuming. The only real advantage over an escalator is that disabled and wheelchair bound passengers find them easier to use.

12.3 The development of escalators

The idea of a 'moving staircase' was investigated towards the end of the nineteenth century with various patents being taken out by Jesse Reno, George Wheeler and Charles Seeburger. The first really viable escalators, based on Seeburger's design, were installed on the London Underground in 1911 at Earl's Court.

These first escalators were followed by twenty more over the next four years and by the mid 1920's, the escalator became well established.

Between the Wars, many escalators were installed to replace older lifts and since that time, the escalator has been established world-wide as the preferred method of high volume transportation of passengers between levels, particularly on busy metros and suburban rail systems.

Fig. 12.1. An early underground escalator.

12.4 Passenger flow to and from escalators and/or lifts

Again reference should be made to Chapter 2 on station planning but a little more is given here. At street or station concourse level, when the tracks are at a lower level, passengers tend to arrive at a steady rate unless they have arrived there by another mode of transport.

At platform level, however passengers arrive in large groups as they alight from stopping trains. Passengers can only board lifts or escalators at a finite rate, and in the case of lifts, only when there is a car at the landing. It is essential therefore that station layouts provide for generous landing areas with capacity to hold large numbers of passengers who are waiting for vertical transportation. For these reasons, large unobstructed landings should be provided at both concourse and platform level, particularly the latter.

Where possible, two alternative means of access to platform level should be provided so that if a machine is out of service at one access point, the other is still available. Multiple access of this type is often found at surface or shallow depth stations but it is very costly to provide this at deep level 'tube' stations.

Where escalators are installed, it is preferable to have three machines in one shaft so that up and down service can be maintained even if one machine is out of use. At stations where there is a 'tidal flow' situation, the three-escalator arrangement also gives an opportunity to reverse one of the escalators at mid-day to give higher capacity with the larger flow. Similarly, this arrangement also helps to keep both up and down service going when replacement of the machines becomes necessary.

Lifts should always, if possible, be installed in pairs, partly to ensure continuity of service in the event of breakdown but also to allow transfer from one car to another in the event of failure between landings.

Failure of an escalator does at least allow its continued use as a fixed stair, albeit at a flow rate of about a third of a moving escalator. However, failure of a lift means that the capacity is lost completely, apart from possibly using adjacent spiral emergency stairs.

12.5 Achievable flow rates for modern lifts

Passengers get a strong perception that lifts, particularly large and deep ones, are slow and inefficient. This is largely brought about by the fact that there is usually a wait for the car to arrive at the start level, another whilst it fills and a further period of inactivity on the part of the passenger whilst it travels to the required level. Escalators however at least give the impression that there is no waiting for arrival or departure and the passenger can even shorten the journey time by walking up!

Passenger flow when using lifts depends upon the size of the car, the height of the rise, speed of travel and the time at the landings.

A medium sized modern station lift car carrying say 32 people might take about 30 s dwell time to empty and fill at landings and would travel at a rate of about 1.5 m/s. In a shaft 35 m deep, the effective round journey time of one car would be about 1.4 min. This would mean that running at capacity, a pair of such lifts could transport about 2750 passengers in an hour.

The flow capacity for this lift arrangement would therefore be only about 46 passengers per minute on average. As all lifts have to go both up and down, capacities must be the same in each direction.

12.6 Flow rates on escalators

If every step of an escalator could be occupied with two standing passengers, it is possible in theory to produce an absolute maximum flow on an escalator of over 200 passengers per minute.

Research has shown that, in fact, this is not possible in practice, even under the most crowded conditions. A number of psychological factors come into play relating to the behaviour of people when crowded together which causes some spacing out to be inevitable. In the most crowded and stressful situations when passengers are hurrying to get out of a station, full scale tests and observations have shown that the maximum possible flow rate that can be achieved is between 120 and 140 passengers per minute.

Even with this high rate, there must be clear space at the top of the escalator to allow people to be able to clear away quickly from the escalator to allow following passengers to be able to step off safely.

For designing stations, it is recommended that a figure of 100 passengers per minute should be used for worst case demand. This means that in normal circumstances, even in peak periods, only one side of the escalator

Fig. 12.2. A modern railway design using escalators and lift.

will have standing passengers, the other side being free for those who wish to walk on.

It will be seen from the foregoing that one moderately full escalator can be expected to carry well over twice as many passengers on average than a pair of lifts. Perhaps even more significantly, it will also be realised that two up escalators can easily clear up to 400 passengers from each train running at a minimum headway of two minutes in the peak which certainly could not be achieved by a bank of four lifts.

12.7 Types of escalators

The escalator basically consists of two continuous chains passing over sprockets at each end and carrying steps. The steps are of approximately triangular cross section and carry a wheel at each corner. The upper wheels are attached to the chain and the lower 'trailer' wheels run independently. A complex system of tracks ensures that the wheels cannot lift off the tracks at critical points of the escalator.

For all practical purposes, the angle of inclination of all modern escalators is 30°.

Escalators that can be used on railways fall into the following three basic types.

- Compact
- Semi-Compact
- Heavy Duty Public Service

12.8 Compact type escalators

These are lightweight, low rise machines such as found in departmental stores and shopping malls. The drive machinery is small and installed inside the step band to save space. Access to all the machinery is through the steps and hence the machine can only be serviced during railway non-traffic hours or when the staircase can be put out of use.

Compact machines can only be of use to a very limited degree on railways because of these restrictions. They can be useful however for street level to ticket level and overhead viaduct applications, provided there is an alternative fixed stair.

The typical service life of a compact machine is 15 to 20 years at the most. As they are a self contained unit, replacement can be carried out very quickly.

Fig. 12.3. Typical semi-compact escalator.

Where these lightweight escalators have been installed in certain cities around the world, mainly for access to metros, the author has noticed that they are often out of service. This is particularly the case when the top of the escalators is open to the weather. Clearly they are not designed for heavy use and this must be taken into consideration in the design stage of any railway.

In any case, it would be wise to involve the manufacturers of these compact machines with the on-going maintenance of these machines on a day-to-day basis.

12.9 Semi-compact type escalators

These are heavier duty machines than the compact, suitable for light railways or Metros. They are more robust than the compact type and are suitable for vertical rises up to about 15 m. The drive machinery is too bulky to fit inside the step band and is mounted adjacent to the upper drive sprocket but still within the escalator structural framework which is usually known as the 'truss'.

The typical service life of a semi-compact type escalator is 20 to 25 years.

As with the compact type, replacement is easier than with the heavy duty machines as the whole escalator breaks down into a small number of self contained pre-wired and equipped units with a minimum of site assembly.

12.10 Heavy duty public service escalators

These are heavy duty machines as installed on the London Underground capable of sustained service and carrying crowded loads to considerable heights and depths.

These HDPS escalators have substantial step chains and drive sprockets and a more robust wheel design and mounting arrangement. The truss is wider and deeper than for the compact types and the drive machinery is mounted external to the truss, above the upper drive sprocket, on a separate bedplate. A separately accessed substantial machine chamber is required to house the drive machinery.

The practical maximum vertical rise for these HDPS machines is in the order of 30 m, although one exists in Budapest with a rise of 38 m. At this height, the total live load can exceed 25 ton which is a great strain on the sprockets, chain and drive machinery.

The typical service life for a heavy duty machine can be expected to be about 40 years although some of the original machines lasted over 60 years before replacement took place. In the last few years, maintenance of these old machines was difficult and expensive however and it is not recommended that modern machines subject to heavy loads should stay in service that long. Also after 40 years, more failures and 'down-time' occurs which badly affects passenger satisfaction and confidence.

The figure below shows a view of a typical heavy duty escalator installed on the London Underground. This is slightly heavier than many installed on other railways world-wide.

Fig. 12.4. Heavy duty public service escalator.

12.11 Typical HDPS escalator dimensions

The following dimensions are given only as a preliminary planning guide. Actual required dimensions must be obtained from manufacturers.

Min. headroom above step nosings	–	2.4 m
Min. length of horiz. steps from comb to intersection with sloped nosing line	–	2.0 m
Length of Upper Machine Chamber	–	12.0 m
Min. depth of Machine Chambers	–	2.5 m
Clear step width between balustrades	–	1.0 m
Average o/a width of pair of trusses	–	1.9 m
Abs. min. centres of Escalators	–	2.5 m
Angle of escalator to the horizontal	–	30°

Dimensions for compact escalators are generally much smaller and vary depending upon type and manufacturer.

12.12 Types of modern lift

There are many types of lift now available today. In engineering terms the most important distinction for railway applications is between traction and hydraulic lifts.

The traction lift has a car suspended by wire ropes from a sheave or grooved pulley at the other end of which is a counterweight. The lift is moved by a motor and reduction gear driving the sheave. The traction lift is faster in operation than the hydraulic lift, has faster journey times and can cope with any height of rise. The maximum rise that is known to the author in a railway application is 55 m.

The hydraulic lift movement is provided by a hydraulic ram mounted below or beside the lift shaft, to which the car is attached. Motive power is provided by a hydraulic pump and valve system. Hydraulic lifts tend to be the cheapest and take up less space. The main disadvantages is that they are relatively slow in operation and have a practical maximum rise of about 17 m.

12.13 Application of lift types

For busy modern stations, vertical transport is better by escalator than lift for reasons given previously. However at less busy or outlying stations or where there are considerable physical site restraints, lifts can be used.

Vertical movement of people in any volume and height above 15 m should always be done by traction lifts with fairly large cars up to a capacity of about 50 people. It is best if possible to provide separate entrance and exit doors at opposite ends of the car to enhance passenger flow at landings.

Lifts for disabled and mobility impaired people are usually much smaller and are hydraulic. It is important that these lifts, although smaller, have wide doorways to ensure that wheelchairs and people with baggage have easy access.

Automatic lifts must have some means of communication from the car to a control room, or at least an alarm that can be operated by passengers in the event of a lift failure or other incident. Wherever possible, lifts should have windows or glazed panels in doors so that passengers can be seen inside the lift car. This is particularly important at unmanned stations and where lifts go from ground level up to an elevated railway station platform.

12.14 Safety risks and human factors

When moving people within station areas by mechanical means, there are risks involved which are different from those when all vertical movement in stations is by foot.

These risks need to be faced and steps taken to reduce them to a practical minimum. Also it needs to be stated however, that the risks are not all on one side. If passengers are required to walk or climb unreasonable distances or heights there is the additional likelihood that normal pedestrian falls and mishaps will be increased, to say nothing of the increased distress that could be unnecessarily caused to the aged and less mobile.

Escalators are probably the most powerful pieces of stationary equipment found in most passenger stations and hence are the most potentially dangerous. The main interfaces between moving and stationary parts are likely to cause the most trouble. These include the following:

- Gaps at the sides of steps, adjacent to skirting panels.
- Gaps between steps, especially at the upper and lower curves.
- Combs at top and bottom landings.
- Handrails.

As well as entrapment of passengers at these locations, the main hazards associated with escalator operation are fire, cascade fall, step collapse and step/comb collision.

There are a number of detectors built into modern escalators to reduce these hazards to a minimum. Emergency stop switches are provided on every escalator which immediately slow down and halt the machine as quickly as possible without precipitating a cascade fall for other passengers.

The main hazards associated with lifts are doors opening between floors, passengers entrapped by doors and loss of control of the car speed. Overspeed detectors are fitted to all lifts which slow and stop the lift should any apparent falling or undue acceleration start.

12.15 Inspection and maintenance

All escalators and lifts must be well maintained and regularly inspected by suitably qualified staff. In the UK, there is a statutory requirement for inspection of lifts and Health and Safety Recommendations for escalators that all machines should be inspected at least every six months. In addition the H&SE recommend periodic examination and function tests of certain critical items at five yearly intervals, notably drive gearboxes and all safety gear.

12.16 Pumps

Chapter 6 includes reference to the track drainage system.

On surface railways, the track drainage collects the surface water and wherever possible channels it either to the nearest watercourse or to Local

Authority storm water drains. In rare cases this is not possible or the railway may itself be subject to flooding or be below the level of the normal water table.

When this is the case, it is usual to drain water by gravity to a holding chamber or sump and, when sufficient water has been collected, it is pumped away to a suitable drain.

Where railways run in tunnels, water may also percolate through the linings or run down the track drainage to a low spot in the tunnel.

Here again water will be collected and pumped away when sufficient has run in.

Pumps in railway drainage sumps are often remote from other railway buildings and may be very inaccessible. They are usually switched on and off by some form of float device which can easily become blocked or fouled by debris, dirt and vegetation.

It is essential that every railway engineering organisation makes clear who is responsible for inspection and maintenance of pumps, sumps, float switches and other associated equipment and lays down the periods when site inspection should be carried out. Because there is some mechanical similarity with lift and escalator equipment, some railways make their Lift and Escalator Engineer also responsible for pumps.

Severe flooding, both in tunnels and on the surface, can disrupt track circuits and signalling as well as causing potential damage to the track structure and must be avoided. Unnecessary delays to trains can be caused by neglect to sumps and pumps and this is a classic case of ' prevention is better than cure'.

Certain pump components do deteriorate with time and use. It is essential that proper spares are kept for these either at site or readily available to maintenance engineers.

At particularly vulnerable sites, it may well be worthwhile to install a second standby pump with a separate supply and float switch which will 'cut-in' in the event of the first pump not functioning. Pumps should also be monitored remotely by an alarm in a control room when sump water levels get too high.

CHAPTER 13

Ventilation and Draught Relief

13.1 Is ventilation a problem on railways?

For surface railways running mainly out in the 'fresh air' it would not appear, at first sight, that ventilation is a concern for today's railway engineer.

This is mainly so, particularly where some form of electric traction is used and where there are only short tunnels or covered ways.

However, where parts of any railway go into tunnel of lengths exceeding about half a mile, then ventilation is an aspect that must be given consideration. For Metros which are mainly underground, good ventilation should be a major consideration.

In the early days of railways, before the introduction of electric traction, ventilation proved to be of great concern where long tunnels existed.

The author has in his possession a bound edition of the *Minutes and Proceedings of the Institution of Civil Engineers Vol. XLIV* for 1876. This volume contains a most interesting paper presented to a meeting of the Institution on 18th January 1876 by Gabriel J Morrison entitled 'The Ventilation and Working of Railway Tunnels'. Incidentally the chair at the meeting was taken by the then President George Robert Stephenson, none the less!

Clearly from the content of the paper and the reported discussion that followed, there was much concern at that time, both on the part of the public and by many practicing railway engineers. This related to the health risks and safety hazards produced by 'impurities generated in tunnels by combustion of fuel'. The main cause for concern was the large amount of carbonic acid coupled with a lesser amount of sulphuric acid that is discharged into the atmosphere by coal fired steam locomotives. The paper includes reference to the crew on a goods train in the Mont Cenis Tunnel having fainted because of 'foulness of air' and to public complaint about the stale air on the Underground section of the Metropolitan Railway in London. Clearly, travelling on the footplate of a steam locomotive, or for that matter in following carriages, was not pleasant in long tunnels.

Modern railways do not now use locomotives which burn coal or coke or run on steam. However, diesel power will continue to be in use for many more years. Where railways are diesel powered and operate underground for part of their route, careful thought needs to be given to the problem of proper ventilation of the exhaust gasses, particularly where trains have to stand for any length of time with engines running. Even large terminal stations which have large 'train shed' roofs can suffer from diesel fume pollution caused by trains waiting to depart.

This chapter includes brief reference to the factors that are involved in tunnel ventilation which can be applied to longer tunnels and covered ways on surface and sub-surface railways as well as to railways which are completely underground.

13.2 Movement of air

The movement of airflow in and around a railway system which is at least partially underground, caused by the piston effect and drag/thrust of the trains, is not an exact science due to the number of variables that exist.

As would be expected, the maximum piston effect of trains is in tunnels which only carry a single track. The minimum clearance between the rolling stock and the tunnel, and the shape of the front of the train, will both effect the amount of air that is pushed along by the train.

For main line trains, the blockage ratio in single line tunnels could be expected to be about 0.5 but for tube trains it can be as high as 0.7. Air movement in twin track tunnels is considerably less.

On an underground system, the amount of air displaced into a station by the piston effect of a single train entering is in most cases no more than the combined cubic capacity of the passageways, escalator shaft and ticket hall. The same train when leaving would tend to suck back after it, the same foul air that it had pushed into the station. It can be seen therefore that this would result in little air change, even in the upper levels and ticket hall, and hardly any in the running tunnels.

The movement of air through the tunnel caused by trains is taken into account when deciding the position of tunnel cooling fans. For an exhaust type ventilation system, fan shafts are usually placed near to the entry end of the platform. This ensures that air taken up the shaft and out to atmosphere has passed through the tunnel from the preceding station and has received a maximum amount of heat from the tunnels. Similarly, pressure type ventilation blows air in at the departing end of the platform so that it is taken into the running tunnels by departing trains and has a cooling and cleansing effect.

Controlled movement and gradual changing of air in long tunnels and underground railways is important for a number of reasons which include the following:

- Removal of 'stale' air with some tunnel dust and introduction of 'fresh' air containing more oxygen.
- Removal of excessive heat generated by train equipment, human bodies, lighting, night engineering works and radiated from surrounding ground and the tunnel walls. This involves cooling tunnel air to a desirable average ambient temperature around 21°C.
- Reduction of uncomfortable draughts.
- Smoke control in the event of fire or smouldering.

13.3 Deciding on exhaust or pressure

As has already been mentioned, ventilation in tunnels can be effected by either exhaust or pressure, sucking out the foul air or blowing in the fresh.

Early tunnel ventilation schemes usually adopted a pressure approach which meant that all fans blew fresh air into the system and the stale air came out at station and tunnel openings. This arrangement meant that you were met by the foul air in your face as you entered a station, giving a false impression of a 'smelly' railway.

In recent years the usual practice has changed to run fans to exhaust, which has in no way affected the general principal of cooling, but gives a considerable improvement for the passenger, who now enters the station with the fresh air drawn in by the fans. In winter, passengers pass smoothly from the cold outer air to the higher temperature at platforms, without usually even noticing that the temperature may have risen by as much as 15°C.

Another point to remember is the need to ventilate lavatories, shops and staff rooms which are below surface level. This type of accommodation is usually ventilated by exhausting from the rooms and drawing the make-up air from the surrounding passages or circulating areas. If these passages are now filled with fresh air entering to feed the exhaust fans, then fresh air is available for the small ventilating plants for the station rooms referred to above. Blowing in cold air direct to running tunnels in the winter can also cause condensation which can effect track circuits and signalling. There are a number of reasons therefore why, generally speaking, it is best to run tunnel fans to exhaust and not to pressure.

13.4 The 'Piston' effect of trains on fans

When considering the construction of a fan with its housing and connecting airways, it is essential to ensure that all the components can withstand the fluctuating surge pressures caused by the passage of trains.

Non-return dampers are used with positive effect to stop the piston action of a passing train from reversing the fan. Without such basic precautions, the train's air volume would stall the fan, with probable disastrous effect on the fan motors and drives.

13.5 Design and operation of tunnel fans

Tunnel cooling fans generally range in size and duty from 10 m^3/s up to as large as 60 m^3/s. During normal operation the two main tasks of tunnel fans is to control the environment by removing heat at night or at other times when trains are not operating and to provide reasonable air movement when a train is stopped in a section of tunnel.

All fans should be designed to be capable of being reversed. With a normal high efficiency axial flow fan, the efficiency will be much less in reverse, possibly as little as 50% of normal running, due to the aerofoil shape of the fan blades. Even with this reduced efficiency, the facility of reversal is very important so that there is complete flexibility in times of emergency.

Large fans running at lower revolutions are usually much more effective than smaller ones running faster. Full life maintenance costs will also be less. It is always best to seek out a location for a larger fan and shaft rather than a number of small shafts with smaller overworked 'screamers'.

Noise and vibration problems are also likely to be much less with larger, slower fans.

Air noise caused by increased velocity through ducts and tunnels can also cause problems where these reach the surface next to domestic buildings.

13.6 Smoke in tunnels

With modern forms of electric traction, there should be no smoke in tunnels under normal operational conditions. Diesel traction does produce some smoke, however which should not be a problem in twin track tunnels although single bore tunnels of any length need to be carefully considered relating to ventilation for normal running.

Smoke on any railway can be a serious hazard in the event of a train or some fixed piece of equipment catching fire. The hazard can affect other trains behind and in front on the same track and also those going in the other direction on an adjacent track or even in another interconnected tunnel. At interchange stations, smoke can also find its way through passageways and shafts to other lines of the same system.

Fans can be used to great effect in removing smoke from tunnels and in moving smoke away from an escape route being taken by passengers who have been detrained from a stalled train.

It is essential when dealing with smoke in tunnels to know the nature of the fire, its exact location in relation to the fixed railway infrastructure and the location of all trains and passengers that could be affected.

Broadly, tunnel fires can be grouped as follows:

- In a running tunnel.
- On a train in a running tunnel.
- On a train in a station tunnel.
- In a station tunnel or passageways.
- Under an escalator.
- In a shaft.

As can be quickly appreciated, if all the relevant facts are not known or if incorrect information is given, it is easy to take the wrong action with fans and make the situation worse.

All modern railways which have appreciable lengths of line in single track tunnels must have a disciplined system of reporting fires and relevant information to central control so that correct action can be taken with tunnel fans where they exist.

It is also essential that a comprehensive fire and smoke alarm system is installed to give early warning of any trouble in vulnerable locations like escalator machine chambers.

13.7 Draught relief

Trains travelling at speed through single track tunnels with small clearances will produce considerable draughts at stations unless some action is taken to reduce them to tolerable levels. Additionally, high air pressure will be experienced in leading cars or coaches of trains unless they are sealed from outside effect.

This effect can be considerably reduced by the introduction of small cross-passages between adjacent single track running tunnels at intervals a little over the length of the longest train using the tunnels. This then allows air to be pushed through the cross-passage into the adjacent tunnel and then back through another cross-passage behind the train as it passes, making a local circulatory path which relieves considerably air pressure ahead of the train.

Also draught relief shafts can be constructed over or alongside the running tunnel which allows air to escape to atmosphere as the train approaches and then to rush down the shaft as the train passes the shaft.

In this case, no fan or dampers are provided at the top of the shaft and strictly speaking it does not materially contribute to the tunnel ventilation system. Draught relief shafts are often located at stations where they have a good effect on reducing high air velocities on platforms. Sometimes shafts which are sunk from the surface to construct a tunnel can be left unfilled to act as draught relief.

On very long bores for railways under water like the Channel Tunnel, ventilation becomes a major consideration. Careful thought needs to be given to the possible 'fire load' and the extent, duration and fierceness of possible fires underground.

In this case, it is very unlikely that intermediate shafts, either for ventilation or for draught relief, can be provided. There is also the problem of moving people from the scene of the fire quickly and safely if the train they are travelling in is on fire.

One solution is to drive a separate service tunnel parallel with the running tunnels and to which it is connected laterally at intervals by cross-passages.

Some form of air-lock or smoke door will be required in these cross-passages which are closed automatically as soon as smoke is detected.

In tunnels of this type which are more than say three miles long, the service tunnel should be large enough to allow emergency service vehicles to drive down and some form of transport to be provided to pick up detrained passengers. The service tunnel will also require a fire main with suitable take-off points to enable any fire or smouldering to be put out as soon as possible after detection.

13.8 Maintenance and inspection of fans

As with all other engineering services, tunnel fans require regular inspection and servicing. Every railway authority needs to set up an organisation to ensure that this is done and a system to ensure that control rooms are informed when fans are out of service for maintenance or major repair.

CHAPTER 14

Future Trends

14.1 The engineering 'Full Circle'

Contemplation of the future is always a risky affair;...but is it, really?

There are many lessons learnt in the hard school of experience, things which touch upon the basics of life, that do not change. Personalities come and go, fashions wax and wane, systems and methods evolve but foundational fundamentals remain intact.

And the same applies to the basics of railway engineering.

The great railway pioneers of the eighteenth century were men of vision, flair and courage; men like Stephenson, Locke, Brunel, Gooch and many others.

But they only achieved their dreams because they were foremost engineers with their feet on the ground. They all respected the basic principles of natural physics within which they had to contend.

All engineers of the present and future should never lose sight of these basic principles which the great engineers of the past followed so doggedly.

As I write the closing pages of this book, the years of the twentieth century are quickly drawing to a close. What will be the future of the railways? Do they have a future?

It is now almost two hundred years since Richard Trevithick's steam locomotive trundled off pulling a train of trucks riding on metal plates. What railway development will be seen in the next two hundred years? Brunel and Stephenson would be amazed if they could see the railways of today and no doubt we would be equally surprised if today we could see the developments of the future.

But I am sure the engineers of the past would recognise immediately the sound fundamentals upon which everything else is built.

They would appreciate, for instance, attractive functional stations, good track, safe signalling, well designed and maintained rolling stock, reliable motive power, and so on.

One has to admit, as well, that there may well be aspects that would not please them, indeed they might well be appalled! If there were such things I am sure it would be where sure and tried principles have been disregarded or where hard learned lessons of the past have been disregarded.

In the early days of railways, it was the visionary engineers like Brunel and Stephenson who were involved at the conception of the idea, pushed the authorising Bill through Parliament and were personally committed to seeing the railway built and operating. Almost the first action that a railway committee would do after formation would be to seek out and appoint the 'Engineer to the Railway'. He would supervise the initial survey, decide the route, design the civil engineering works required and oversee design of the locomotives and rolling stock. He truly was the Engineer for the line.

Over the years, as railways have become more diverse and technically complicated, this over-arching roll has been divided. Within most railways there have been individuals who have taken the lead in their own engineering discipline and the operation of trains has been usually supervised separately from engineering departments.

This specialisation was inevitable and did allow railways to be served by the best qualified engineers in the various disciplines. Indeed, railways have been in the forefront of development of new engineering methods and techniques in the last two hundred years and have produced many outstanding engineers in their particular specialisms.

In any organisation however, any movement towards specialism faces the potential loss of the ability to keep a balanced overall view of things. In recent years, there has been a growing tendency to encourage engineers not to become too specialised but to gain a general appreciation of all the engineering factors and considerations involved in operation of a railway.

So it can be said, to some degree, that engineering in railways has come full-circle.

14.2 The trend towards broader vision

This change in attitude can bring nothing but good to the individuals concerned and the general health of the railway industry as a whole. All engineers should take every opportunity to expand their understanding of the objectives and methods of other engineering disciplines.

All railway engineers also need to realise that railway operation is not a separate mystique quite separate from their own activities but one which is intrinsically bound up with them.

If I might speak from personal experience for a moment, I am most thankful that my career led me from bridges and structures to track and then to overall control of civil engineering before becoming a director of all engineering operations and then Managing Director of all railway activities. That progression gave me an insight into many areas of activity and appreciation of all that is involved, which is so necessary for the 'top job'.

14.3 The trend towards local accountability

With this tendency towards a broader view there is also an encouragement towards becoming more locally accountable. Large 'umbrella' organisations can encourage individuals to be over protective of their own particular interest and to be unyielding or even unco-operative towards other legitimate interests. A good example of this might be the vital interface between permanent way and signalling. Clearly there needs to be co-operation and 'give-and-take' when dealing with signal equipment or wire bonds fixed to and supported by track sleepers.

Many railways known to the author have divided up their large engineering departments in recent years, puting people of different disciplines into locally accountable groups.

This certainly does have the advantage of encouragement of local co-operation and appreciation of other people's local problems.

As with all forms of organisation, however there are also some disadvantages which must be watched. The main potential problem relates to the necessity to guard against variation of standards across the board, because of local pressures or problems. If individuals in the various disciplines have reporting lines outside their discipline, then there needs to be both a separate standard setter and an 'auditor' for each discipline at the centre. There also needs to be some way of passing on information on new developments and techniques so that all individuals can be kept up to date, particularly in highly technical areas.

14.4 Increasing use of information technology

Throughout this book, the essential importance of well monitored inspection and maintenance has been stressed repeatedly. In the past, most areas of activity have relied heavily on manually kept records, experience and memory. With the great possibilities now available through computers, all such records and reminders can now be provided through Information Technology (IT). The setting up of such systems and data collection will be time consuming and expensive but must be faced by all railways in the near future.

There are now also many possibilities which have not yet been fully grasped which IT can provide for railway engineering. Annual inspection and maintenance programmes can easily be produced by computer once all the data has been fed in. Updating of these programmes as work is carried out throughout the year can now be simply produced.

Integration of records can also been achieved as never before using IT, thus allowing better planning of works, scarce resources and railway possessions.

The systems should also be able to give early warning of work peaks that are likely ahead. This could be particularly useful where certain components which have a long life-span will all come up for replacement at the same time, having all been installed when a particular line or extension was built or equipped.

14.5 Improved interchange between transport modes

World-wide there is increased concern that the motor car is choking the life of cities and large towns both by fume emission and by ever increasing demand for road space.

Some form of public transport must be the ultimate answer, probably rail-borne.

The upturn in the use of light rail in many cities around the world during the past decade has begged the question — 'was the demise of the tram so inevitable, after all?' This trend towards rapid transport systems, and in particular light rail, is likely to continue with increasing pace, providing financial backing is forthcoming.

Perhaps the area where there has been the least progress in recent years is improvement in inter-modal transfer. There are many cities, both in the UK and abroard, where transfer from one form of transport to another is difficult, slow and non 'user-friendly'. This applies equally to transfer from private to public and between different forms of public transport.

Transfer to public and private transport at airports for instance is notoriously bad and must cause much 'hassle' as well as loosing countless millions of work hours each year.

From a passenger's point of view, the mode of transport used for any particular journey will be influenced by many considerations, not the least of which is convenience coupled with reliability. The popularity of driving 'door-to-door' in a private car is obvious and will win over most alternatives because there are no changes of mode required, no lugging of cases and no draughty waits. A journey of any length or complexity is likely to involve more than one mode of transport and it is at the points of transfer that most delays and frustration occur.

In my opinion, this whole subject of interchange must be aggressively addressed in the next few years if rail transport is again to demonstrate itself as one of the best forms of transport, particularly in medium haul journeys of say up to three hundred miles. This will involve planners and engineers in looking at journey patterns between cities and within them for the next century.

14.6 A move towards designing for maintenance

Certainly in recent years more thought has been given to maintaining both the railway infrastructure and the rolling stock. There has been an increase in the use of components which can be replaced after an estimated life-span rather than seeking to mend or refurbish such components. This trend should now work its way through to all areas including track.

14.7 Trends in comfort standards

Since the Second World War, people have become accustomed to much higher standards of comfort both in their homes and in their offices. This includes higher controlled temperatures in the winter and often some form of air conditioning or cooling in summer as well as other protection from the elements in circulating areas. Shopping malls and other 'umbrella' developments and modern international airports are good illustrations of this. Railways in the future must improve standards both in station buildings, interchange areas and on trains, in this respect.

Railway engineers must be in the forefront of all these changes and need to update their ideas in their own areas.

CHAPTER 15

Conclusion

15.1 Retrospect

As I sit in my study at home in the Cotswolds, I look back to the time when the idea of this book first began to take root. All I can say is, ...

'it seemed a good idea at the time!'

That probably was about three years before the time of writing this last chapter and possibly about four years before the book will appear in print.

One of my other interests that occupies all too little of my time in partial retirement, is watercolour painting. I find that one of the frustrations of this hobby is looking at the finished work and reflecting in your mind the comment that most of us remember from school report days...

'Could do better'!

As I look at this now almost finished effort on railway engineering I can see all the gaps and the inadequacies and am tempted to start again.

On reflection however, I realise that this is how all engineers have felt about their work down the years. Indeed it was because of this feeling of 'I could do better' that railway engineers have seen such progress in the past two centuries.

Inadequate as it is therefore, I leave this book as it is, trusting that it will at least be a stepping stone for the reader towards better things.

The task of writing this book has not been easy and I record here again those who have helped in so many ways and who are mentioned in the Acknowledgements at the front of this book.

In particular, I mention Professor Tony Ridley who encouraged me to write this book in the first place and under whose direction I now lecture at Imperial College. It was he who appointed me as Director of Civil Engineering at London Transport in 1980 and asked me to take on Docklands Light Railway as the first MD in 1986. These two appointments gave me a great opportunity to widen my scope and I am most grateful for the trust placed in me at that time. As I look back, I also realise that it was Tony Ridley who encouraged me to take a broader view of things and I want to pass this on to those who follow.

15.2 Postscript

If students and young engineers who pick up this book are encouraged to take a wider view, my efforts will have been worthwhile.

Robert Louis Stevenson was a great novelist known and read around the world. He was brought up in a family of engineers, where the great discoveries and engineering achievements of the eighteenth century were well understood and appreciated.

R L Stevenson wrote...

> 'the duty of an engineer is twofold — to design the work and to see that the work is done'.

Well over a hundred years later, these words still apply. Railway engineers occupied in all areas of engineering activity and in management must look to their design to see that it is 'fit for purpose'.

Perhaps even more important, they need to ensure that their designs are translated into reality and that others following will be able to maintain what they have built to keep trains running and passengers happy.

Subject Index